Legal Notice

BOOKS FROM THE GET 800 COLLECTION FOR COLLEGE BOUND STUDENTS

28 SAT Math Lessons to Improve Your Score in One Month
New SAT Math Problems arranged by Topic and Difficulty Level
320 SAT Math Problems arranged by Topic and Difficulty Level
1000 SAT Math Problems arranged by Topic and Difficulty Level
SAT Verbal Prep Book for Reading and Writing Mastery
320 SAT Math Subject Test Problems
    Level 1 Test
    Level 2 Test
320 SAT Chemistry Subject Test Problems
28 ACT Math Lessons to Improve Your Score in One Month
28 ACT Science Lessons to Improve Your Score in One Month
320 ACT Math Problems arranged by Topic and Difficulty Level
320 GRE Math Problems arranged by Topic and Difficulty Level
320 AP Calculus AB Problems
320 AP Calculus BC Problems
Physics Mastery for Advanced High School Students
400 SAT Physics Subject Test and AP Physics Problems
SHSAT Verbal Prep Book to Improve Your Score in Two Months
555 Geometry Problems for High School Students
Pure Mathematics for Beginners
Set Theory for Beginners
Abstract Algebra for Beginners
Topology for Beginners
Real Analysis for Beginners

CONNECT WITH DR. STEVE WARNER

www.facebook.com/SATPrepGet800

www.youtube.com/TheSATMathPrep

www.twitter.com/SATPrepGet800

www.linkedin.com/in/DrSteveWarner

www.pinterest.com/SATPrepGet800

plus.google.com/+SteveWarnerPhD

28 ACT Science
Lessons to Improve
Your Score in One Month

Dr. Robin Satty
Edited by Dr. Steve Warner

Table of Contents

ACTIONS TO COMPLETE BEFORE YOU READ THIS BOOK

1. **Take a practice ACT from the Real ACT Prep Guide to get your preliminary ACT science score**

   Make a note of your score, so that you can keep track of your improvement.

2. **Register for updates**

   Visit the following webpage and enter your email address to receive additional content when it becomes available.

   # www.satprepget800.com/28LeSci

3. **'Like' my Facebook page**

   This page is updated regularly with ACT prep advice, tips, tricks, strategies, and practice problems.

   # www.facebook.com/SATPrepGet800

INTRODUCTION
STUDYING FOR SUCCESS

This book is for anyone who wants to improve their score in ACT Science.

In my experience as a tutor, I have noticed students getting intimidated by the ACT Science section. Students often approach ACT Science in the same way they would approach a science class. However, the skills required to do well in ACT Science are not the same as the skills required to do well in a science class. My goal is to help you see that ACT Science is no more difficult than the other ACT sections; in fact, with just a little training, you will discover that it is actually quite predictable.

This book can help you boost your ACT Science score in one month, as long as you study a little bit each day.

Using this book effectively

- Practice ACT Science questions twenty minutes each day.
- Choose a consistent study time and location.

You will retain much more of what you study if you study in short bursts rather than if you try to tackle everything at once. So, try to choose about a twenty-minute block of time that you will dedicate to ACT Science each day. Make it a habit. The results are well worth this small time commitment. Some students will be able to complete each lesson within this twenty-minute block of time. If it takes you longer than twenty minutes to complete a lesson, you can stop when twenty minutes are up and then complete the lesson the following day. At the very least, take a nice long break, and then finish the lesson later that same day.

- Every time you get a question wrong, **mark it off, no matter what your mistake**.
- Begin each lesson by redoing all the problems from the previous lessons in the same domain that you have marked off. For example, before you begin the lesson "Data Analysis: Reading a Figure," review the marked off questions in the previous Data Analysis lessons, which were "Data Analysis: Reading a Table" and "Data Analysis: Reading a Graph."
- If you get a problem wrong again, **keep it marked off**.

Test-Taking Strategies

1. Mark it Up

At the risk of sounding like your English teacher, I want to emphasize that you really should be marking up your page when answering questions. Make annotations. Jot down notes. I don't mean when reading, though. Mark up the questions! There are many details that look similar and are very easy to mix up.

- Circle names of tables and figures mentioned in questions, such as "Figure 1" or "Table 3."
- Underline names of variables or other details that will direct you to the right line, point, or value, such as "Trial 7" or "$NaNO_3$."
- If you need to use a trend to find the answer, jot down the trend, such as "dist. ↑ conc. ↓." (which stands for "As distance increased, concentration decreased.")
- If you need to remember multiple details, jot them down, such as "S1 under, S2 over" (which stands for "Student 1 argued that it happened underground and Student 2 argued that it happened on top of the surface.)

8

Here is an example:

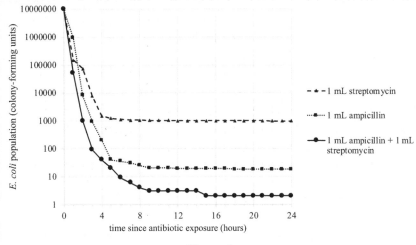

Figure 1

1. According to Figure 1, which antibiotic or antibiotic combination was most effective at reducing the number of colony-forming units of *E. coli* after 20 hours?

   A. 1 mL streptomycin
   B. 1 mL ampicillin
   C. 1 mL ampicillin + 1 mL streptomycin
   D. 1 mL penicillin

Even without having a passage or graph to look at, there are plenty of details that you already know might be important. You can't underline everything. Actually, you can underline everything, but it wouldn't be very helpful. Instead, circle the names of figures and underline other important details. It might look like this:

1. According to Figure 1 which antibiotic or antibiotic combination was most effective at reducing the number of colony-forming units of *E. coli* after 20 hours at 37°C?

You'll notice I didn't underline "colony-forming units", "E. coli", or "37°C". I'll explain why on the next page.

2. Consider What's Unnecessary

The ACT *loves* to try to confuse you by putting unnecessary information in the questions. Sometimes, they'll write out the entire description of a variable, which can take up a whole line or two, when they are really only asking you for "the thing on the *y*-axis". Keep this in mind. Depending on your reading strategy, that might mean anything from ignoring it completely and assuming they're asking for something straightforward, to quickly going back into the passage to confirm the information. For example, if the question says the temperature is 22°C, and there is no mention of temperature anywhere on the graph, you can probably assume the whole experiment was done at 22°C. (This does not apply to questions that start with "Suppose...," which you'll learn more about in Chapter 16: Extrapolating.)

- Look for information about which table(s) or figure(s) to use.
- Read the axis labels and key.
- Cross out words in the question that are also in an axis label.
- If you have time, confirm any additional variables.

Let's look back at the same example as before.

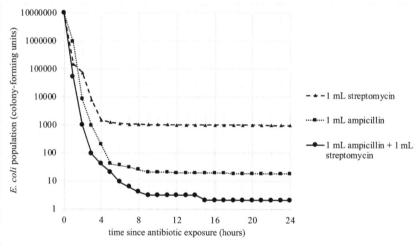

Figure 1

1. According to Figure 1, which antibiotic or antibiotic combination was most effective at reducing the number of colony-forming units of *E. coli* after 20 hours at 37°C?

   A. 1 mL streptomycin
   B. 1 mL ampicillin
   C. 1 mL ampicillin + 1 mL streptomycin
   D. 1 mL penicillin

First, read the question. You should circle "Figure 1" right away. Then, underline key information, which includes "most effective at reducing" and "20 hours". The unnecessary information here is "colony-forming units of E. coli" and "at 37°C", which you can cross out.

How do you know it's unimportant?

Take a look at Figure 1, which is mentioned in the question. The y-axis is "E. coli population (colony-forming units)" and the x-axis is "time since antibiotic exposure (hours)". The key lists some big words.

Look back at the question. The answer choices appear to match the graph key, so when the question says "which antibiotic", you can infer that the graph key and answer choices are all antibiotics or antibiotic combinations. "Colony-forming units of E. coli" matches the y-axis, so you can ignore it completely!

The next piece of information is "20 hours". Since you know the x-axis is time in hours, you know to look at 20 hours.

Lastly, you see "37°C". Temperature isn't mentioned anywhere on the figure, so (if you have time) scan the passage for "37°C" or any other mention of temperature. If there were a passage here, it would mention that the flasks were stored at 37°C, which is not important to the question at all.

Once you cross out the unnecessary information, you're left with:

1. According to Figure 1, which antibiotic ~~or antibiotic combination~~ was most effective at reducing ~~the number of colony-forming units of E. coli~~ after 20 hours ~~at 37°C?~~

Now, all you need to do is look at Figure 1 and see which line shows the biggest decrease at 20 hours.

When you're first learning to consider what's unnecessary, you may find yourself reading the question, looking back at the graphs, rereading the question, looking at the passage, and then realizing you've spent more time on the question than you would have in the first place. That's normal when you first learn a new strategy. With practice, you will get an instinct for picking out the unnecessary information the first time you read the question, even if you haven't looked at the passage or graphs at all.

3. Guess

Even the best students, who are consistently scoring 36 on practice tests, may need to guess on a question or two. Most students will guess on 3-5 questions per test.

The best thing you can do is learn when to let it go. If you spend several minutes working on a question and still end up guessing, you've wasted several minutes for nothing. Learn to recognize when it's just not happening. One guess won't make or break your score. Spending several minutes on a question and then guessing can really hurt your score. If this is done multiple times during the exam, it can take a lot of time away from actually answering questions.

If you haven't eliminated any choices, there are a couple of strategies that can improve your odds of guessing correctly. First, if all else fails, pick A or F. From 2017-2020, A and F were correct answers about 28% of the time. That is a greater chance than randomly picking, which leaves you at a 25% chance of getting the answer correct.

Conversely, some tutors and students swear by a more thoughtful guessing strategy that involves counting up all of your previous answer choices and guessing the letter you've chosen least so far. My opinion is: if you have enough time to do that, you have enough time to actually answer the question.

In summary:

- Pick A/F.

Guess when you:

- are out of time and have to pick something.
- think it will take too long to figure out the answer.
- think it will take too long and you still won't figure out the answer.

4. Scan for Word Shapes

This is a tip I learned from a test prep colleague and mentor, Phil McCaffrey of 3RPrep. If you are looking for information in the text, it's easy to get held up trying to read and understand the text. When looking for key words, forget what's going on in the passage. Focus on the shape of the word you need. Think about what a word like "moon" looks like. It's short and flat, with two circles in the middle. Think about what a word like "Cretaceous" looks like. It's unusually long and mostly flat, with a capital letter at the beginning and only one other tall-ish letter. It is also easier to find information this way by starting at the end of the passage and working backwards, since you are less likely to get distracted by the actual words. Using this strategy—with practice, of course—can help you find information in the text quickly.

Reading Strategies

The most challenging part of the ACT Science section is not the science. It's not the graphs. It's not even the reading. It is, most certainly, time management. If you go in without a strategy, you will likely run out of time. If you want to complete all six passages (or more, or less, depending on whether there are any changes in the coming years) with enough time to carefully consider every single one of the 40 questions, you need to approach the section with a strategy.

I've met tutors who swear by one section strategy or another for every single student. That doesn't work for me. Every student is different. Below are several different strategies for approaching the passages in the ACT Science section. I will also offer suggestions for which strategy will be best for *your* goal, whether that's a 26 or 36 or anything in between.

All strategies require practice. Pick one you think will work and try it on a few official ACT practice tests before deciding it's your favorite.

1. Don't Read

The biggest challenge in the ACT Science section is time management. For students who struggle with time management, the best strategy may be to skip the reading completely! Believe it or not, you won't find that many answers in the text. Only about a quarter of the answers are found directly in the text, and even some of those can be inferred from the tables and figures.

You can probably answer between one half and three quarters of the questions without even looking in the text at all. The remaining questions are almost always the most difficult ones. Depending on your timing, you can scan the passage for the answers to those questions or you can guess answers for those questions and move on.

When to Use

- Your goal is 30 or less.
- You don't have a lot of time to study.
- You are running out of time using one of the other strategies.
- You are getting bogged down by the difficult content and it's making it harder to interpret the graphs.

How to Attack

- Skip the reading and go right to the questions.
- Look for clues about which table, graph, or figure to use:
  - "According to Study 1"
  - "In Experiment 3"
  - "In Figure 1"
  - "From Tables 1 and 2"
- Ignore technical words in questions; look only for the words that are row or column headings, axis labels, or variables on graph keys.
- If you need more information, look back in the passage only if you have enough time.
- If you don't have time to look back in the passage, make an inference based on the graphs and your background knowledge.

Practice the Strategy

I left out the reading for this passage on purpose, to model the strategy. If you're really interested in reading it, you can look ahead to the other reading strategies. However, I'd like you to trust me for a few minutes and see that you can answer most of the questions without even seeing the text. Try each question before looking at the answer below it.

Passage I

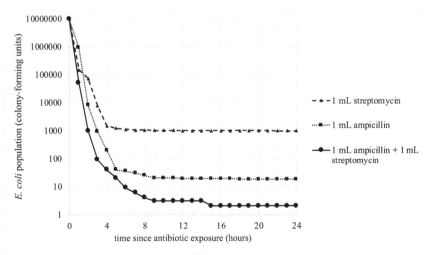

Figure 1

1. According to Figure 1, which antibiotic or antibiotic combination was most effective at reducing the number of colony-forming units of *E. coli* after 20 hours at 37°C?

   A. 1 mL streptomycin
   B. 1 mL ampicillin
   C. 1 mL ampicillin + 1 mL streptomycin
   D. 1 mL penicillin

Answer: C. In Figure 1, the y-axis shows colony-forming units of *E. coli*. The x-axis shows time. Find 20 hours on the x-axis and find the line that is the lowest, because that shows the population that has been reduced the most. The lowest line is the solid line with circles, which is the population that got 1 mL ampicillin + 1 mL streptomycin. Ignore 37°, because temperature isn't mentioned anywhere.

2. Consider the data in Figure 1. From hour 0 to hour 24, the population of *E. coli* exposed to 1 mL streptomycin:

   F. increased only.
   G. decreased only.
   H. increased, then decreased.
   J. decreased, then increased.

Answer: G. In Figure 1, the y-axis shows population. The streptomycin line is dashed with triangles (it is the highest line on the graph) and only decreased as time passed from hour 0 to hour 24, from left to right across the x-axis. Although the line looks fairly flat on the right half of the graph, it is still showing a very slow decrease.

3. Suppose the scientist had continued measuring the population in each flask for two additional hours. At 26 hours, the population of *E. coli* in the flask that had received 1 mL ampicillin would most likely have been:

   A. less than 2 colony-forming units.
   B. between 2 colony-forming units and 10 colony-forming units.
   C. between 10 colony-forming unit and 100 colony-forming units.
   D. greater than 100 colony-forming units.

Answer: C. In Figure 1, the y-axis shows population. The ampicillin line is dotted with squares (it is the line appearing in the middle on the graph) and only decreased as time passed from hour 0 to 24, from left to right across the x-axis. The line is decreasing very, very slowly at hour 24, when the population is just above 10. In 2 more hours, the population will likely continue to decrease very, very slowly and still be above 10.

4. Which variable was kept constant for all flasks in the experiment?
   F. Number of colony-forming units after 24 hours
   G. Type of antibiotic added
   H. Amount of antibiotic added
   J. Incubation temperature

Answer: J. The number of colony-forming units (F) are shown on the y-axis of Figure 1, so that is likely the dependent variable, which is not kept constant. The type of antibiotic (G), and amount of antibiotic (H) are listed in the key as different between the different groups in the experiment, so they are also not kept the same between groups. The only remaining answer is **J**, which is not mentioned at all on the graphs. You won't know it's the answer for sure, but you can make a solid inference without looking at the passage.

(If you don't remember what the words "variable" and "constant" mean, I will review that in Lesson 3: Experimental Design. While I have your attention, I want to warn you that you won't have all the information you need to answer the next two questions. The "Don't Read" strategy works for most of the questions, but not all of them. I am including the questions anyway because you do have enough information to eliminate some of the wrong answer choices.)

5. Which of the following statements is best supported by the information in the passage and Figure 1?
   A. The most bacteria grow in a flask with two antibiotics combined.
   B. Bactericidal antibiotics are most harmful to humans.
   C. The antibiotics will kill every single one of the bacteria.
   D. The fastest way to kill bacteria is with bactericidal antibiotics.

Answer: B or D. In Figure 1, the flask with the two antibiotics combined (solid line with circles) had the smallest population (y-axis) after 24 hours (x-axis), so we can eliminate choice **A**. None of the lines goes all the way down to 0, so none of the antibiotics kill every single one of the bacteria. Therefore, we can eliminate choice **C**. The remaining choices use words that do not appear on the graph and are probably in the passage. If you have extra time, go back and look in the passage, but if not, pick one and move on.

6. The scientist predicted that bactericidal antibiotics are more effective when combined than when used separately. Are the results in Figure 1 consistent with this prediction?

   F. Yes; the population of *E. coli* decreased the most in 24 hours after exposure to both ampicillin and streptomycin.
   G. Yes; the population of *E. coli* decreased the most in 24 hours after exposure to ampicillin only.
   H. No; the population of *E. coli* decreased the most in 24 hours after exposure to both ampicillin and streptomycin.
   J. No; the population of *E. coli* decreased the most in 24 hours after exposure to ampicillin only.

Answer: F. You don't know what bactericidal antibiotics are, but you can infer that "combined" refers to ampicillin + streptomycin. In Figure 1, the combination (solid line with circles) had the lowest population of *E. coli* (y-axis) remaining after 24 hours (x-axis), so the combination is likely most effective. You are also inferring that the "goal" is for antibiotics to kill the most bacteria.

2. Read a Little

Much of the reading on the ACT (in Science and in Reading) follows the school rule that the first sentence in a paragraph has to give the main idea of the paragraph. Reading the first sentence of each paragraph serves two purposes: (i) you get the main idea of the paragraph and (ii) you have an idea where to look in the text for answers.

By reading—and understanding—the first sentence of each paragraph, you will be able to answer about 90% of the questions. You will also know where to find the answers to the remaining 10% and be able to find them faster.

When to Use

- Your goal is a score between 30 and 34, and you want the chance of getting lucky with a 36.
- You don't get overwhelmed by unfamiliar science words.
- You are getting all the data analysis and science content questions right, but still want to improve your score.
- You are running out of time or getting confused when reading the entire passage.

How to Attack

- Read the first sentence of every paragraph.
- Make note of where key definitions are located.
- Make note of where experiments are described.
- Make assumptions but confirm technical words in the questions.

Practice the Strategy

Once again, try each question before looking at the answer below it.

Passage I

A scientist investigated the effects of combining bactericidal antibiotics, which work by killing bacteria directly. (This is where the rest of the passage would be. Skip it.)

Next, antibiotics were added to each flask and the flasks were stored in an incubator at 37°C. (Skip the rest of the paragraph.)

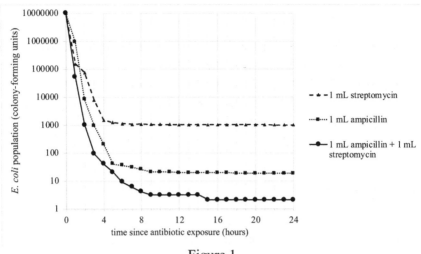

Figure 1

1. According to Figure 1, which antibiotic or antibiotic combination was most effective at reducing the number of colony-forming units of *E. coli* after 20 hours at 37°C?

   A. 1 mL streptomycin
   B. 1 mL ampicillin
   C. 1 mL ampicillin + 1 mL streptomycin
   D. 1 mL penicillin

Answer: C. Based on the reading you did, you know that the question is asking which antibiotic or antibiotic combination was working the best at killing bacteria by 20 hours. You can confirm that 37°C is unnecessary information because, according to the text, all flasks are at 37°C. In Figure 1, the *y*-axis shows colony-forming units of *E. coli*. The *x*-axis shows time. Find 20 hours on the *x*-axis and find the line that is the lowest, because that shows the population that has been reduced the most. The lowest line is the solid line with circles, which is the population that got 1 mL ampicillin + 1 mL streptomycin.

2. Consider the data in Figure 1. From hour 0 to hour 24, the population of *E. coli* exposed to 1 mL streptomycin:

   F. increased only.
   G. decreased only.
   H. increased, then decreased.
   J. decreased, then increased.

20

Answer: G. In Figure 1, the *y*-axis shows population. The streptomycin line is dashed with triangles (it is the highest line on the graph) and only decreased as time passed from hour 0 to hour 24, from left to right across the *x*-axis. Although the line looks fairly flat on the right half of the graph, it is still showing a very slow decrease.

3. Suppose the scientist had continued measuring the population in each flask for two additional hours. At 26 hours, the population of *E. coli* in the flask that had received 1 mL ampicillin would most likely have been:

A. less than 2 colony-forming units.
B. between 2 colony-forming units and 10 colony-forming units.
C. between 10 colony-forming unit and 100 colony-forming units.
D. greater than 100 colony-forming units.

Answer: C. In Figure 1, the *y*-axis shows population. The ampicillin line is dotted with squares (it is the line appearing in the middle on the graph) and only decreased as time passed from hour 0 to 24, from left to right across the *x*-axis. The line is decreasing very, very slowly at hour 24, when the population is just above 10. In 2 more hours, the population will likely continue to decrease very, very slowly and still be above 10.

4. Which variable was kept constant for all flasks in the experiment?

F. Number of colony-forming units after 24 hours
G. Type of antibiotic added
H. Amount of antibiotic added
J. Incubation temperature

Answer: J. This is the first question you can answer more quickly after reading the first sentence of each paragraph. A constant is something that is the same between experimental groups. According to the text, "the flasks were stored in an incubator at 37°C," so temperature was constant.

5. Which of the following statements is best supported by the information in the passage and Figure 1?

A. The most bacteria grow in a flask with two antibiotics combined.
B. Bactericidal antibiotics are most harmful to humans.
C. The antibiotics will kill every single one of the bacteria.
D. The fastest way to kill bacteria is with bactericidal antibiotics.

21

Answer: B or D. In Figure 1, the flask with the two antibiotics combined (solid line with circles) had the smallest population (y-axis) after 24 hours (x-axis), so we can eliminate choice **A**. None of the lines goes all the way down to 0, so none of the antibiotics kill every single one of the bacteria. Therefore, we can eliminate choice **C**. The first sentence in the passage states that bactericidal antibiotics "work by killing bacteria directly," which implies there is a less direct option. Since humans are never mentioned, you can infer that **D** is the best answer. If you have extra time, you can read more in the passage to confirm, using the first sentences as a hint for where to look.

6. The scientist predicted that bactericidal antibiotics are more effective when combined than when used separately. Are the results in Figure 1 consistent with this prediction?

   F. Yes; the population of *E. coli* decreased the most in 24 hours after exposure to both ampicillin and streptomycin.
   G. Yes; the population of *E. coli* decreased the most in 24 hours after exposure to ampicillin only.
   H. No; the population of *E. coli* decreased the most in 24 hours after exposure to both ampicillin and streptomycin.
   J. No; the population of *E. coli* decreased the most in 24 hours after exposure to ampicillin only.

Answer: F. According to the passage, "bactericidal antibiotics "work by killing bacteria directly." You don't know which antibiotics are bactericidal, but you can infer that "combined" refers to ampicillin + streptomycin. In Figure 1, the combination (solid line with circles) had the lowest population of *E. coli* (y-axis) remaining after 24 hours (x-axis), so the combination is likely most effective. You are also inferring that the "goal" is for antibiotics to kill the most bacteria.

3. Read a Lot

Reading everything is surprisingly similar to only reading the first sentence of every paragraph. Since the first sentence often covers the main idea, the first sentence of each paragraph is often all you really need to understand. The rest of the reading is there to give you a general idea of what is going on, some definitions, and a hint of where to find answers in the text.

The hardest part of this strategy is getting used to not understanding every last word. If you are looking for a 36, you are probably not the kind of student who is used to reading without comprehension. Get used to it. If you take the time to understand every word, you will run out of time. Only read slowly enough to get a general idea of what is going on, learn what words are defined, and make note of where key information can be found. You don't even need to remember the definitions or key information. If the right words show up in a question, you'll know exactly where to go to find the definition, fact, relationship, or experimental variable.

When to Use

- Your goal is a 34 or higher.
- You are getting all of the data analysis and science content questions right, but still want to improve your score.
- You are a quick reader.
- You are comfortable moving through a reading even if you don't understand everything.

How to Attack

- Read and understand the first sentence.
- Skim the rest of the paragraph, making note of where you see any definitions, key information, or experimental variables.
- Repeat until you get to the end of the passage.
- Skip tables and graphs until you get to the questions.

Practice the Strategy

At this point, you've seen the questions already. It's worth taking another look so you can see exactly what text helps you and what text is unnecessary. The explanations are different from the explanations in the previous sections because they take the reading into account. It's worth reading through them so you know how you might approach the questions differently if you've read the text.

Passage I

A scientist investigated the effects of combining bactericidal antibiotics, which work by killing bacteria directly. This is in comparison to bacteriostatic antibiotics, which work by inhibiting bacterial growth and tend to act more slowly. The two bactericidal antibiotics studied were ampicillin and streptomycin. The scientist added 200 mL of nutrient broth to three identical flasks, which were then inoculated with a population of rapidly growing *Escherichia coli*.

Next, antibiotics were added to each flask and the flasks were stored in an incubator at 37°C. Each hour, a 1 mL sample of the nutrient broth would be treated using a serial dilution with additional sterile nutrient broth and spread evenly on sterile Petri dishes with nutrient agar. The dishes were kept in the incubator for 48 hours, after which the populations were calculated. The data were graphed in Figure 1.

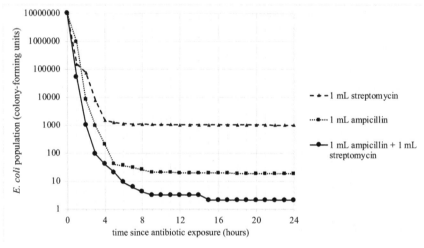

Figure 1

1. According to Figure 1, which antibiotic or antibiotic combination was most effective at reducing the number of colony-forming units of *E. coli* after 20 hours at 37°C?

   A. 1 mL streptomycin
   B. 1 mL ampicillin
   C. 1 mL ampicillin + 1 mL streptomycin
   D. 1 mL penicillin

Answer: C. Based on the reading, we know that the question is asking which antibiotic or antibiotic combination was working the best at killing bacteria by 20 hours. The information 37°C is unnecessary because according to the text all flasks are at 37°C. In Figure 1, the y-axis shows colony-forming units of *E. coli*. The x-axis shows time. Find 20 hours on the x-axis and find the line that is the lowest, because that shows the population that has been reduced the most. The lowest line is the solid line with circles, which is the population that got 1 mL ampicillin + 1 mL streptomycin.

2. Consider the data in Figure 1. From hour 0 to hour 24, the population of *E. coli* exposed to 1 mL streptomycin:

    F. increased only.
    G. decreased only.
    H. increased, then decreased.
    J. decreased, then increased.

Answer: G. In Figure 1, the y-axis shows population. The streptomycin line is dashed with triangles and only decreased as time passed from hour 0 to 24, from left to right across the x-axis. Although the line looks fairly flat on the right half of the graph, it is still showing a very slow decrease.

3. Suppose the scientist had continued measuring the population in each flask for two additional hours. At 26 hours, the population of *E. coli* in the flask that had received 1 mL ampicillin would most likely have been:

    A. less than 2 colony-forming units.
    B. between 2 colony-forming units and 10 colony-forming units.
    C. between 10 colony-forming unit and 100 colony-forming units.
    D. greater than 100 colony-forming units.

Answer: C. In Figure 1, the y-axis shows population. The ampicillin line is dotted with squares and only decreased as time passed from hour 0 to 24, from left to right across the x-axis. The line is decreasing very, very slowly at hour 24, when the population is just above 10. In two more hours, the population will likely continue to decrease very, very slowly and still be above 10.

4. Which variable was kept constant for all flasks in the experiment?

    F. Number of colony-forming units after 24 hours
    G. Type of antibiotic added
    H. Amount of antibiotic added
    J. Incubation temperature

Answer: J. A constant is something that is the same among experimental groups. According to the text, "the flasks were stored in an incubator at 37°C," so temperature was constant.

5. Which of the following statements is best supported by the information in the passage and Figure 1?

    A. The most bacteria grow in a flask with two antibiotics combined.
    B. Bactericidal antibiotics are most harmful to humans.
    C. The antibiotics will kill every single one of the bacteria.
    D. The fastest way to kill bacteria is with bactericidal antibiotics.

Answer: D In Figure 1, the flask with the two antibiotics combined (solid line with circles) had the smallest population (y-axis) after 24 hours (x-axis), so you can eliminate choice A. None of the lines goes all the way down to 0, so none of the antibiotics kill every single one of the bacteria. Eliminate choice C. The first sentence in the passage states that bactericidal antibiotics "work by killing bacteria directly," which implies there is a less direct option. Scan the passage for the word "humans," and you'll see that they are never mentioned, so eliminate choice B. Choice **D** is the best answer. This can be confirmed by looking in the text where it says "This is in comparison to bacteriostatic antibiotics, which work...more slowly."

6. The scientist predicted that bactericidal antibiotics are more effective when combined than when used separately. Are the results in Figure 1 consistent with this prediction?

    F. Yes; the population of *E. coli* decreased the most in 24 hours after exposure to both ampicillin and streptomycin.
    G. Yes; the population of *E. coli* decreased the most in 24 hours after exposure to ampicillin only.
    H. No; the population of *E. coli* decreased the most in 24 hours after exposure to both ampicillin and streptomycin.
    J. No; the population of *E. coli* decreased the most in 24 hours after exposure to ampicillin only.

Answer: F. According to the passage, "bactericidal antibiotics "work by killing bacteria directly" and the bactericidal antibiotics were ampicillin and streptomycin, the two chemicals listed in the graph key. By reading the passage, we know for sure that both of those antibiotics are bactericidal, which makes it easier to answer the question confidently. In Figure 1, the combination (solid line with circles) had the lowest population of *E. coli* (y-axis) remaining after 24 hours (x-axis), so the combination is likely most effective. We are also inferring that the "goal" is for antibiotics to kill the most bacteria.

LESSON 1
READING: FINDING IN THE TEXT

Although the ACT Science writers really seem to like their tables and figures, more than 10% of the questions can be answered using the text. In fact, the answers are often stated explicitly in the text, using similar (or sometimes identical!) words as the question. The hard part is figuring out what the question is asking and where to find the answer.

These types of questions show up most often in the conflicting viewpoints passages (the ones with a lot of text and few figures). However, these questions don't require an understanding of the arguments or any of the content; all you need is to find the right detail in the right paragraph.

Sometimes questions require finding a concept in the text and then applying it to a table or figure. Those types of questions are usually straightforward data analysis questions, so I will be focusing on the reading comprehension aspect here.

How to Recognize

- Buzz words: based on _____'s explanation, which students/scientists would be likely to agree?
- The question is asking about a concept or definition described in the text.
- In a conflicting viewpoint passage, the question will almost always refer to the name of the argument you should refer to (such as "Student 1").

How to Attack

- Circle the argument name ("Student 1", "Scientist 3") if it's mentioned in the question.
- Underline key vocabulary words in the question that tell you where to look.
- Look back in the passage where you remember reading about that concept or scan the passage for the key words.

28

Don't Get Tricked

- Sometimes questions look like they're asking about science knowledge, but the answer is in the text.

Try to answer the following question using this strategy. **Do not** check the solution until you have attempted this question yourself.

LEVEL 1: FINDING IN THE TEXT

Passage I

Endocrine disruptors are chemicals that can affect development and reproduction in humans and other mammals. Endocrine disruptors can be present in food or can leach into food and liquids from containers. Scientists performed three experiments to explore the presence of such chemicals in frozen soup, frozen pasta, and frozen pizza from five food brands.

Experiment 1

Scientists analyzed frozen food for the presence of the following chemicals: bisphenol A (BPA), diethyl phthalate (DEP), and dimethyl phthalate (DMP). Gas- and liquid-chromatography were used to identify the presence of these chemicals in ten different samples of food from each brand after being thawed at a temperature of 22°C for 24 hours. The frequency of each chemical was calculated for each brand as a ratio of number of food samples for one brand with the chemical present to the number of total food samples for that brand.

Experiment 2

Scientists took one food sample from each brand that had all three chemicals present and found the concentration of each chemical in parts per million (ppm).

Experiment 3

Scientists filled a BPA-containing plastic cup with 100 mL of distilled water (H_2O). The cup was stored at a temperature of 22°C. The concentration of BPA that leached out of the cup and into the water was measured every six hours for one week. The experiment was then repeated at temperatures of 25°C, 30°C, 35°C, and 40°C.

29

1. Which experiments, if any, involved finding the concentration of chemicals?

   A. Experiment 1 only
   B. Experiment 2 only
   C. Experiments 2 and 3 only
   D. None of the experiments

Solution: The key word here is "concentration." Scan the text for the word "concentration." Experiment 1 found the frequency of each chemical, which is mentioned in the last sentence of Experiment 1. Frequency is not the same as concentration. In Experiment 2, the scientists "found the concentration." In the second sentence of Experiment 1, "the concentration of BPA that leached out of the cup and into the water was measured." Since "concentration" appears as being measured or found in Experiments 2 and 3, the answer is choice **C**.

Let's practice a bit more. Answer these questions by finding the answer in the text. Questions 2-4 refer to Passage I above. Questions 5-8 refer to Passage II, which can be found after Question 4. The answers to these questions, followed by full solutions, are at the end of this lesson. **Do not** look at the answers until you have attempted these questions yourself. Please remember to mark off any problems you get wrong.

LEVEL 1: FINDING IN THE TEXT

2. Which temperature was not used during Experiment 3?

   F. 25°C
   G. 30°C
   H. 32°C
   J. 35°C

LEVEL 2: FINDING IN THE TEXT

3. In Experiment 2, which endocrine disruptors were present in every food sample tested?

> I. BPA
> II. DEP
> III. DMP

A. I only
B. I and II only
C. II and III only
D. I, II, and III

4. How did Experiment 1 differ from Experiment 3? In Experiment 1:

F. temperature was kept the same, but in Experiment 3, temperature was varied.

G. temperature varied, but in Experiment 3, temperature stayed the same.

H. only one chemical was tested, but in Experiment 3, several chemicals were tested.

J. BPA was tested, but in Experiment 3, several chemicals were tested.

Passage II

Viruses are microscopic and consist of an inner nucleic acid core surrounded by a protein capsid. Viruses are many times smaller than bacteria. Scientists have long debated whether viruses should be classified as living organisms. Viruses reproduce by infecting a host cell and using the cell's machinery to replicate its genetic material and produce proteins.

Student 1

Properties of living organisms include: movement, respiration, growth, response to environment, excretion, nutrition, and reproduction. Anything that has any three or more of these characteristics is a living organism. Viruses respond to the environment and reproduce only. Viruses do not have three of these characteristics independent of a host, so they are not living organisms.

31

Student 2

Properties of living organisms include: movement, respiration, growth, response to environment, excretion, nutrition, and reproduction. Something must have all of these characteristics to be considered a living organism. Viruses do not perform respiration, so they are not living organisms.

Student 3

Properties of living organisms consist only of: movement, growth, response to environment, and reproduction. Anything that has all of these characteristics is a living organism. Although viruses require a host to reproduce, reproduction occurs nonetheless, so viruses are living organisms.

Student 4

I agree with Student 3, except that viruses are not living because they cannot reproduce on their own.

5. Which of the following phrases best describes a major point of difference between Student 3's and Student 4's viewpoints?

   A. The properties of living organisms
   B. The classification of viruses
   C. The ability of viruses to reproduce on their own
   D. The host species of virus reproduction

LEVEL 3: FINDING IN THE TEXT

6. How would the classification of viruses differ from that described in Student 1's viewpoint if viruses showed movement, growth, and response to environment only? According to Student 1, viruses would:

   F. perform respiration
   G. reproduce on their own
   H. be considered living organisms
   J. not be considered living organisms

LEVEL 4: FINDING IN THE TEXT

7. Student 4's viewpoint indicates that an organism is not living if it does not:

A. perform respiration.
B. excrete waste.
C. respond to its environment.
D. reproduce with the aid of a host.

8. According to Student 1's viewpoint, a virus:

F. performs photosynthesis.
G. does not perform respiration.
H. should be considered a living organism.
J. is larger than a bacterium.

Answers

1. C	5. B
2. H	6. H
3. D	7. C
4. F	8. G

Full Solutions

2.

At the end of the description of Experiment 3, all of the listed temperatures were mentioned except for 32°C, so the answer is choice **H**.

3.

In Experiment 2, the text states that the scientists used samples "that had all three chemicals present." The chemicals are listed in Experiment 1 as the same three listed in the answer choices, so the answer is choice **D**.

33

4.

Scan the answer choices to see that the question is asking about whether temperature or number of chemicals varied. In Experiment 1, the food was "thawed at a temperature of 22°C." In Experiment 3, the experiment was repeated at different temperatures (last line of the text), so the answer is choice **F**.

5.

Student 4 states directly that "I agree with Student 3, except," so you know the answer immediately follows. Student 4 then says "viruses are not living because they cannot reproduce on their own." The point of disagreement is not whether viruses can reproduce on their own (choice **C**) because Student 3 says "viruses require a host to reproduce." The point of difference is whether viruses are living organisms, which is the classification of viruses, choice **B**.

6.

According to Student 1, something needs three or more of the listed characteristics. Movement, growth, and response to environment are all listed as characteristics of life in the first sentence of Student 1's argument, so viruses would be considered living organisms, choice **H**.

7.

Student 4 agrees with Student 3. Student 3 states that living things must have the following properties: movement, growth, response to environment, and reproduction. Thus, something that does not respond to its environment is not living, choice **C**.

8.

Student 1 states that "Viruses respond to the environment and reproduce only" and need three or more of the listed characteristics to be considered alive. Student 1 also states that viruses "are not living organisms," so they do not have any additional characteristic. Since performing respiration would be a third characteristic, according to Student 1, viruses do not perform respiration, choice **G**.

LESSON 2
DATA ANALYSIS: READING A TABLE

Reading a Table is the second most common type of question in the ACT Science section, so it's definitely an important one to master. These types of questions will usually give you directions on where in the table you need to look. It's surprisingly simple, but also very easy to mess up.

How to Recognize

- Buzz words: table, based on, results of experiment, results of study
- The question will almost always refer to the name of the table you should use (such as "Table 1") or the column headings on that table.

How to Attack

- Circle the table name if it's mentioned in the question.
- Circle details in the question that tell you where to look on the table (column headings, row headings, values).
- Go to the right table.
- Find the right column(s) and/or row(s).

Don't Get Tricked

- It's easy to look at the wrong column or row in a table. Tracing with your pencil every time can help.

Try to answer the following question using this strategy. **Do not** check the solution until you have attempted this question yourself.

LEVEL 1: READING A TABLE

Passage I

Titration	Volume HCl (mL)	Volume of NaOH added (mL)
1	50.0	30.2
2	50.0	29.8
3	50.0	30.1
4	75.0	44.6
5	75.0	45.3

1. According to the table, which titration used the greatest volume of NaOH?

   A. Titration 2
   B. Titration 3
   C. Titration 4
   D. Titration 5

Solution: The key words here are "greatest" and "volume of NaOH". Volume of NaOH is the title of the rightmost column in the table. The largest number in that column is 45.3, which is in the bottom row of the table. Follow the bottom row all the way to the row title on the far left, which is Titration 5. This is choice **D**.

Let's practice a bit more. Answer the following questions by finding the answer in the table. Questions 2-4 refer to Passage I above. Questions 5-8 refer to Passage II, which can be found after Question 4. The answers to these questions, followed by full solutions, are at the end of this lesson. **Do not** look at the answers until you have attempted these questions yourself. Please remember to mark off any problems you get wrong.

LEVEL 1: READING A TABLE

2. How much HCl was used in Titration 2?

F. 29.8 mL
G. 30.1 mL
H. 44.6 mL
J. 50.0 mL

LEVEL 2: READING A TABLE

3. The average volume of NaOH required to titrate 75.0 mL HCl was closest to:

A. 30.0 mL
B. 45.0 mL
C. 50.0 mL
D. 75.0 mL

4. Which titration used the volume of NaOH closest to the volume of NaOH used in Trial 5?

F. Trial 1
G. Trial 2
H. Trial 3
J. Trial 4

Passage II

Students conducted an experiment to see how gravity affected toy cars rolling down a ramp. A 1-meter long ramp was set up at a 15° angle with the flat table. Five different cars, each with a different mass, were rolled down the ramp. The time it took for the car to roll down the entire ramp was measured with a stopwatch. The experiment was then repeated with ramp angles of 30° and 45° (see Table 1). The results of the experiment are shown in Table 2.

37

Table 1	
Trial	Ramp Angle
1	15°
2	30°
3	45°

Table 2			
	Time (sec)		
Car Mass (g)	Trial 1	Trial 2	Trial 3
150	32.3	29.5	21.1
175	32.0	29.3	20.9
250	31.2	28.5	20.2
300	29.8	26.7	18.7
375	28.4	24.8	16.8

5. According to Tables 1 and 2, the fastest trial occurred with which mass and ramp angle?

	Car Mass	Ramp Angle
A.	150 g	15°
B.	150 g	45°
C.	375 g	15°
D.	375 g	45°

6. What was the mass of the car that rolled down the ramp the most slowly during all 3 trials?

F. 150 g
G. 175 g
H. 300 g
J. 375 g

LEVEL 3: READING A TABLE

7. Based on Tables 1 and 2, at which ramp angles did the 175g car roll down the ramp in less than 30 seconds?

A. 15°, only
B. 45°, only
C. 30° and 45°, only
D. 15°, 30°, and 45°

8. The 375g car rolled down the 15° ramp in the same amount of time as the car with which mass, in grams, rolled down the 30° ramp?

F. 175 g
G. 250 g
H. 300 g
J. 375 g

Answers

1. D	5. D
2. J	6. F
3. B	7. C
4. J	8. G

Full Solutions

2.
According to the table, Titration 2 (second row of data from top) used 50 mL of HCl (middle column), which is answer choice **J.** The other answer choices consist of numbers that appear in the wrong column (the rightmost column).

3.
This question involves a little higher order thinking, because you have to estimate an average of 2 values from the table. According to the table, 75.0 mL HCl (middle column) was used in Titrations 4 and 5 (bottom two rows). The volume of NaOH used in those titrations (rightmost column) was 44.6 and 45.3. We don't need to calculate an exact average, because the answer choices are pretty far apart., We can estimate that the average is around 45 mL. The answer is choice **B.**

4.

According to the table, Titration 5 (bottom row) used 45.3 mL of NaOH (rightmost column). The closest number to 45.3 in the rightmost column of the table is 44.6, which is the NaOH used for Titration 4, choice **J**.

5.

Scan Table 2 for the lowest time, because fastest means shortest time. The smallest number is 16.8 in the bottom right corner, which corresponds to 375 g and Trial 3. If you look back at Table 1, you see Trial 3 is a 45° angle. Therefore, the answer is choice **D**.

6.

"Most slowly" means longest time. You want the mass (leftmost column in Table 2) that had the highest time for each trial (each column). The highest time for each trial was in the top row of data, which corresponds to the 150 g car, choice **F**.

7.

In Table 2, the 175 g car is the second row of data. The 175 g car had under 30 seconds for the rightmost two columns, which are Trials 2 and 3. According to Table 1, Trials 2 and 3 had angles of 30° and 45°, respectively, choice **C**.

8.

According to Table 1, the 15° ramp was used in Trial 1 (top row of data). According to Table 2, the 375 g car rolled down the ramp during Trial 1 (second column of table and leftmost column of data) in 28.4 seconds. There are no other 28.4-second trials, but there is a 28.5 second trial for the 250 g car (middle row of data) in Trial 2 (second column from right). According to Table 1, Trial 2 used a 30° ramp, so the answer is 250 g, choice.

LESSON 3
SCIENCE CONTENT: EXPERIMENTAL DESIGN

Experimental Design is the Scientific Method. It is scientific communication. This is what scientists do and how they think. Understanding the experimental design process will not only help you answer questions that are directly about the process, but will also help you answer questions that address any part of an experiment or scientific argument.

Since so many questions can be answered using information in the passage and graphs, your first line of attack should always be to look and see if the answer is given to you. If you did a good job skimming the passage, then you should have no trouble remembering where the experiment description is. If you have time, always look back in the passage first, but don't forget that sometimes the answer isn't there. These questions might require a few more seconds of skimming for information that isn't there, but you shouldn't be rereading the entire passage.

A few times per test, the answer isn't given in the passage or graphs. You'll need to use your own knowledge of experimental design to answer these questions. Think about definitions that might help you, starting with any important words in the question that aren't defined in the passage. Think about how you can use the definitions to answer the questions.

The trickiest questions can be the ones that require common sense. About one question per test actually requires a combination of experimental design knowledge and common sense to answer. The hardest part is to identify the question, step out of your standardized test mode, and actually use common sense.

How to Recognize

- Buzz Words: hypothesis, independent and dependent variable, experimental and control groups, constant, validity
- Asking about what the scientist(s) investigated, how they investigated it, or why they investigated it that way

How to Attack

- Scan the experiment description to see if the information is stated in the passage.
- Think through relevant experimental design definitions.
- Apply definitions to the question.
- If all else fails, use common sense.

What to Know

Science begins with a **hypothesis**, which is a logical inference based on prior research and scientific knowledge. An **experiment** is designed to test a hypothesis and should include exactly one **independent variable** (or input) and one or more **dependent variables** (or outputs). A **variable** is something that can change. Ideally, an experiment includes two samples or groups: an **experimental group**, which receives the "treatment" that is being tested, and a **control**, which does not. The control is often the sample, group, or trial that gets 0 of something or the normal amount of something.

The experimental and control groups should differ only by the independent variable, but all other factors should remain **constant** (the same). The greater the **sample size** or the larger the number of repetitions, the more reliable the results, since they are less likely to be caused by randomness or error.

A scientist analyzes the data collected from the experiment and draws a **conclusion**, which will state whether the hypothesis was or was not supported by the experiment. If a hypothesis is tested many, many times and repeated by many, many scientists, with the same conclusion every time, that hypothesis becomes a **theory**. Scientists look into the data as a whole, often looking at general trends and averages, and sometimes eliminating **outliers**, or a few data points that are very far off from the rest and could be due to error.

For example, let's say a scientist wants to see whether a medicine is effective at treating headaches. That scientist would find many people with headaches, who are as similar to each other as possible. Half of those people, the experimental group, will receive the medicine, while the other half (the control group) receives a **placebo**. A placebo is a treatment that looks and feels like the experimental treatment, but doesn't have the actual treatment in it. The idea behind a placebo is that the people involved in the experiment don't know whether they are getting the medicine or not, as this knowledge might affect the results. In this experiment, the independent variable is whether people received medicine or placebo and the dependent variable is what happened to their headaches.

Try to answer the following questions using this information. **Do not** check the solution until you have attempted this question yourself.

LEVEL 1: EXPERIMENTAL DESIGN

Passage I

Experiment

A 500 gram sample of soil was collected from a research site. A series of nested sieves were used to separate soil particles by size. In each trial, the following steps were performed:

1. A 50 gram sample of uniformly-sized particles was added to a glass cylinder with a diameter of 3 cm and a fine mesh filter covering the bottom.
2. The soil was left to settle for 24 hours.
3. The cylinder was suspended above a graduated cylinder.
4. 100 mL of water (H_2O) was added to the cylinder and a timer was started.
5. Water was collected in the graduated cylinder until droplets stopped falling.
6. The timer was stopped and the amount of water in the graduated cylinder was recorded.

The table below shows, for each trial, the size range of soil particles and the time it took for the water to filter through the soil, along with the amount of water collected.

Trial	Particle size (mm)	Filtration time (seconds)	Water collected (mL)
1	<1 mm	252	92
2	1-3 mm	102	98
3	>3 mm	19	99

1. Which of the following pieces of equipment would have best allowed the scientists to find the mass of the soil sample after the filtration was complete?

   A. Balance
   B. Microscope
   C. Graduated cylinder
   D. Spectroscope

Solution: The question is asking for a device that measures mass. Mass is measured by a balance, choice **A**.

Notes: A microscope (B) is used for seeing very small objects, such as bacteria or cells. A graduated cylinder (C) is used for measuring volume. A spectroscope (D) is used for measuring the different wavelengths in light.

LEVEL 2: EXPERIMENTAL DESIGN

2. The scientists intentionally kept which of the following factors the same in all trials?

   F. Cylinder diameter
   G. Particle size
   H. Filtration time
   J. Volume of water collected

Solution: The question is asking for a constant or controlled variable, although you don't need to know those terms to answer the question. Step 1 of the experiment states that a 3 cm diameter glass cylinder was used and the steps were repeated for all trials. Thus, cylinder diameter was constant, or stayed the same, for all trials. This is choice **F**.

Note: We can also answer this question through process of elimination. Since choices G, H, and J each appear as a column heading on the table, each one is an independent or dependent variable. Therefore, each of these factors was **not** kept the same in all the trials.

Try to answer these questions based on what you remember from the start of the chapter. Once you have given them a try, go back into the chapter and look up anything you're still not sure about. Questions 3-4 refer to Passage I above. Questions 5-8 refer to Passage II, which can be found after Question 4. The answers to these questions, followed by full solutions, are at the end of this lesson. **Do not** look at the answers until you have attempted these questions yourself. Please remember to mark off any problems you get wrong.

LEVEL 2: EXPERIMENTAL DESIGN

3. The scientists intentionally varied the:

    A. Soil sample mass
    B. Particle size
    C. Filtration time
    D. Cylinder diameter

LEVEL 3: EXPERIMENTAL DESIGN

4. Which of the following was a dependent variable in the experiment?

    F. Particle size
    G. Volume of water collected
    H. Soil sample mass
    J. Cylinder diameter

Passage II

Drosophila melanogaster is a species of fruit fly that is often used for genetic research because its genome is well-studied. CX15 is a strain of *D. melanogaster* with a mutation affecting lifespan. Scientists wanted to investigate what other factors were affected by the CX15 mutation.

45

Study

Scientists collected 100 wild-type *D. melanogaster* and 100 CX15 *D. melanogaster*. The scientists then built identical fly habitats and put 5g of a yeast-based food in each habitat. Ten flies—a random combination of juvenile and mature *D. melanogaster*—from the same strain (either wild type only or CX15 only) were put into each habitat. The mass of remaining food was found every 24 hours for one week, at which point flies began to die and the experiment was ended.

5. Which of the following pieces of equipment did the scientists most likely use to measure the dependent variable during the study?

   A. Graduated cylinder
   B. Balance
   C. Microscope
   D. pH meter

LEVEL 4: EXPERIMENTAL DESIGN

6. Which strain of *D. melanogaster* was most likely the control?

   F. CX15, because it included the mutation scientists wanted to investigate.
   G. CX15, because it did not include the mutation scientists wanted to investigate.
   H. Wild type, because it did not include the mutation scientists wanted to investigate.
   J. Wild type, because it included the mutation scientists wanted to investigate.

7. Which of the following could the scientists have done to improve their experiment?

   A. Use 1,000 wild-type *D. melanogaster* flies only and no CX15 *D. melanogaster* flies.
   B. Use 1,000 CX15 *D. melanogaster* flies only and no wild-type *D. melanogaster* flies.
   C. Start with the same number of juvenile and mature *D. melanogaster* flies in each habitat.
   D. Use a different type of food.

LEVEL 5: EXPERIMENTAL DESIGN

8. Why did the scientists most likely end the experiment when they did?

   F. The D. melanogaster population was no longer the same in each habitat.
   G. The wild-type D. melanogaster flies had begun to develop the CX15 mutation.
   H. The presence of dead D. melanogaster flies would cause the remaining flies to eat less.
   J. Only the CX15 D. melanogaster flies were dying.

Answers

1. A	5. C
2. G	6. H
3. B	7. C
4. G	8. F

Full Solutions

3.

The question is looking for the independent or manipulated variable, which is often found in the leftmost column of data in a table. In the experiment, the scientists were looking at how particle size affected filtration time and volume, so particle size was intentionally varied. This is choice **B**.

4.

The dependent variable is the measured variable or output of the experiment, and is usually found towards the right side of a table. Step 6 states that at the end of the experiment, time was stopped and the volume of water was recorded. The two rightmost columns in the table are "Filtration time" and "Water collected". Thus, the dependent variables were filtration time and water collected, but only one of those (**C**) is the answer.

47

5.

The dependent variable is the measured variable or output of the experiment. Scientists measured the mass of food remaining. Mass is measured using a balance, choice **B**.

6.

The scientists were investigating the CX15 mutants. The control was the "normal" group, which in this case was the wild-type group, choice **H**.

7.

Choices A and B suggest larger samples, which can make an experiment better, but they are suggesting removing either the experimental or control group. Choice D would not make the experiment better or worse based on the information in the passage. Choice **C** would control an additional variable, the number of each age flies, so it would improve the experiment. Therefore, the answer is choice **C**.

8.

According to the last sentence of the text, scientists ended the experiment when flies began to die. In the experiment, the number of flies in each habitat was intentionally held constant (10). Once the flies began to die, this number was longer constant. So, the answer is choice **F**.

LESSON 4
READING: EXPERIMENTAL PARAMETERS IN TEXT

An experimental parameter is a number or other detail that helps define the experiment. These questions appear to be reading comprehension questions, but they're much easier than that! They often require you to identify a single detail in a description of an experiment. It's less about reading to understand and more about picking the right word or phrase to use. You don't need to understand anything outside of that word or phrase.

The answers to these questions are often found in the first few sentences of the experiment description or in a numbered list of steps. When there are multiple experiments in a passage, the first sentence of the descriptions of Experiment 2 or Study 2 will often start with something like, "Experiment 1 was repeated except..." and whatever follows the "except" is the answer to a question about the difference between the experiments.

A healthy understanding of experimental design and "Scientific Method" vocabulary is helpful, but not necessary for these types of questions. In this lesson, questions that require specialized knowledge are not included; these can be found in Lesson 3.

How to Recognize

- Buzz words: based on the description of Study/Experiment, variable, control, constant, factor, varied
- The question will often be asking about factors that varied or stayed the same between different experiments or different experimental groups.

How to Attack

- Circle the experiment, study, or step number if it's mentioned.
- Underline key vocabulary words in the question that tell you where to look.
- If you are not told specifically where to look, scan the passage for key words.

Don't Get Tricked

- If a question refers to a specific step number in an experiment, your answer should only consider that step, and not any steps before or after.
- If you can find the answer by looking at the axes or key on a graph, do that instead—that is often a faster way to identify factors that are different or the same among experimental groups

Try to answer the following questions using this strategy. **Do not** check the solution until you have attempted this question yourself.

LEVEL 1: EXPERIMENTAL PARAMETERS

Passage I

Students wanted to investigate the acceleration of various objects in freefall. All experiments were done from a platform suspended 50 m above the ground. Students on the platform synced stopwatches with students on the ground below.

Experiment 1

Students dropped spheres from the platform and measured the time they took to reach the ground. The spheres were all 5 cm in diameter, but varied in mass.

Experiment 2

Students repeated Experiment 1, except they used spheres that varied in diameter but each had a mass of 150 g.

Experiment 3

Students repeated Experiment 2, except they used objects of various shapes.

1. What was the shape of the objects used in Experiment 2?
   - **A.** Cubes
   - **B.** Spheres
   - **C.** Cylinders
   - **D.** Various shapes

Solution: This question asks about Experiment 2, so look for the answer there. Experiment 2 has the statement, "they used spheres," so the answer is choice **B**.

Try to answer these questions with the information in the text, but don't spend time trying to understand everything in the passage. Questions 2-4 refer to Passage I above. Questions 5-8 refer to Passage II, which can be found after Question 4. The answers to these questions, followed by full solutions, are at the end of this lesson. **Do not** look at the answers until you have attempted these questions yourself. Please remember to mark off any problems you get wrong.

LEVEL 1: EXPERIMENTAL PARAMETERS

2. In Experiments 1, 2, and 3, how far did each object fall?

F. 25 m
G. 50 m
H. 100 m
J. 200 m

LEVEL 2: EXPERIMENTAL PARAMETERS

3. Which factor was varied in experiments 1 and 2?

	Experiment 1	Experiment 2
A.	shape	mass
B.	mass	shape
C.	mass	diameter
D.	diameter	mass

4. What was the mass of the objects used in Experiment 1?

F. 5 g
G. 50 g
H. 150 g
J. The masses varied.

LEVEL 3: EXPERIMENTAL PARAMETERS

Passage II

Three studies examined how various *abiotic* (nonliving) and *biotic* (living) factors affected the growth of several species of frog in a South American rainforest ecosystem

Study 1

For each species A, B, and C, the following steps were performed:
1. A cage with a volume of 1.5 m^3 was left in the same location in a frog habitat with a 50 g mixture of local insects as bait.
2. Once a frog entered the cage, an automatic locking mechanism would seal the frog in the cage.
3. The cage was brought to the nearby research station, where the frog was measured and tagged.
4. No more than 60 minutes later, the frog was released at the same site it had been captured.
5. Steps 1-4 were repeated until 50 frogs had been measured.

Study 2

Study 1 was repeated, except with 100 frogs of Species A. In addition to recording mass and length, scientists also recorded whether frogs were juvenile or adult.

Study 3

Scientists wanted to see how the presence of nitrogen in soil affected the growth of different rainforest frog species. Experiment 1 was repeated for Species A and B, using 50 of each frog species from each of two habitats, Site 1 and Site 2, which had different amounts of nitrogen in the soil.

5. Which factor stayed the same in Study 1 but varied in Study 3?
   A. Frog species
   B. Location
   C. Frog age
   D. Frog length

6. Study 2 was used to study the:

    F. size differences between frogs of different species.
    G. size differences between frogs of different ages.
    H. difference in soil nitrogen content at different locations.
    J. difference in biotic factors in different ecosystems.

LEVEL 4: EXPERIMENTAL PARAMETERS

7. How many total frogs were measured in Study 1?

    A. 50 frogs
    B. 60 frogs
    C. 150 frogs
    D. 200 frogs

8. The primary difference between Studies 2 and 3 is that in Study 2:

    F. scientists looked at different species of frog,
        but in Study 3, scientists looked at different locations.
    G. scientists looked at different locations, but in
        Study 3, scientists looked at different species of frog.
    H. scientists looked at different species of frog,
        but in Study 3, scientists looked at only one species of frog.
    J. scientists looked at only one species of frog,
        but in Study 3, scientists looked at different species of frog.

Answers

1. B	5. B
2. G	6. G
3. C	7. C
4. J	8. J

Full Solutions

2.

In the first paragraph, the text states the platform was "50 m from the ground." Experiment 1 describes in the first sentence how students dropped objects from the platform and they hit the ground, so the objects fell 50 m. This is choice **G**.

3.

Make sure you're looking at the right experiments. Skim Experiments 1 and 2 for the word "varied". In Experiment 1, the objects "varied in mass" and in Experiment 2, the objects "varied in diameter." This is choice **C**. Make sure you don't mix up the two experiments. Jot down notes if you need to.

4.

Make sure you're looking at the right experiment. In Experiment 1, the text states the objects "varied in mass." So, the answer is choice **J**.

5.

Both Study 1 and Study 3 used more than one species of frog, so eliminate A. Neither study mentioned frog age, so eliminate C. Length was measured, so it wouldn't be the same (D). **B** is the answer because Study 3 used two different locations but Study 1 trapped all of the frogs in the same location.

6.

Make sure you're looking at the right study. Study 2 mentions that scientists recorded the frogs' mass, length, and age (juvenile or adult). All frogs were from the same species and same location, so F, H, and J can't be correct. The answer is **G**.

7.

In Study 1, 50 frogs *of each species* were caught. There were 3 species, so the total number of frogs was 3x50=150 frogs (**C**).

8.

If you glance at the answer choices, you see they're talking about the number of species and number of locations. In Study 2, the frogs were all Species A and there was no mention of location. In Study 3, scientists looked at Species A and Species B, and two different locations. Choice **J** is correct because it states that Study 2 used one species of frog but Study 3 used more than one species of frog.

LESSON 5
DATA ANALYSIS: READING A GRAPH

This section contains the most common type of question in the ACT Science section. The answer to this type of question is explicitly represented in one of the given graphs about 15% of the time. That's almost one in every six questions, on average, although in practice it usually works out to be several questions among just two or three of the passages. Keep in mind that this question type includes only those questions whose answers are found directly on the graph, as opposed to questions that require you to describe a trend, make an inference, or extrapolate.

How to Recognize

- Buzz words: graph, based on, results of experiment, results of study
- This type of question will almost always refer to the name of the graph you should use (such as "Figure 1") or the axis labels on that graph.

How to Attack

- Circle the graph name if it's mentioned in the question.
- Circle details in the question that tell you where to look on the graph (axis labels, values).
- Go to the correct graph and find the correct line, bar, or wedge.
- Circle the correct point and trace it back to the x-axis or y-axis to find the correct value.

Don't Get Tricked

- Carefully read the key to make sure you're looking at the correct line. Think to yourself "dotted line with black triangles," or whatever kind of line it is, so you don't get mixed up. Trace the line with your pencil.
- Sometimes the right and left y-axes are labeled differently and refer to different lines.

- Sometimes a question will ask you for the opposite of what the graph says. For example, a graph might show percent of surviving rabbits but the question might ask for percent of rabbits that died.

Try to answer the following questions using this strategy. **Do not** check the solution until you have attempted this question yourself.

LEVEL 1: READING A GRAPH

Passage I

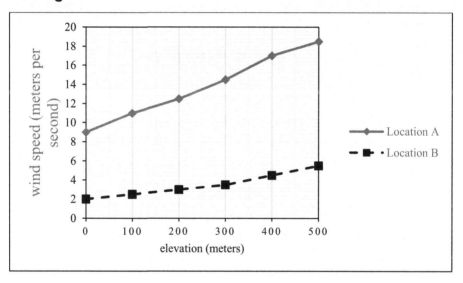

1. According to the figure, the wind speed at Location B at an elevation of 400 meters was closest to which of the following values?

   A. 2 meters per second
   B. 4 meters per second
   C. 9 meters per second
   D. 17 meters per second

Solution: The goal here is to find the correct point on the graph. The question wants the wind speed (which is labeled on the y-axis), at Location B, at 400 meters. The key on the right side of the graph shows us that Location B is represented by the dashed line with squares. If we follow the x-axis (horizontal axis) to 400, then move up from 400 until we hit the dashed line with squares, and then move over to the y-axis where it lines up with the square above 400, we see that the wind speed is around 4 meters per second, choice **B**.

Try to answer the following questions using the information given in the graphs. You will not see any text because you often don't need text to help you answer these types of questions. Questions 2-4 refer to Passage I above. Questions 5-8 refer to Passage II, which can be found after Question 4. The answers to these questions, followed by full solutions, are at the end of this lesson. **Do not** look at the answers until you have attempted these questions yourself. Please remember to mark off any problems you get wrong.

LEVEL 2: READING A GRAPH

2. According to the figure, the wind speed on the ground at Location A was closest to which of the following values?

   F. 2 meters per second
   G. 5.5 meters per second
   H. 9 meters per second
   J. 18.5 meters per second

LEVEL 3: READING A GRAPH

3. Consider the statement "For each 100-meter increase in elevation, the wind speed also increased." This statement is consistent with the data in the figure for which location, if either?

   A. Location A only
   B. Location B only
   C. Both Location A and Location B
   D. Neither Location A nor Location B

4. Suppose a company wants to build a 100-meter tall wind turbine designed to convert wind power into electricity. Based on the figure, which of the two locations should the company choose in order to maximize the wind exposure at that elevation?

    F. Location A; the wind speed at Location A at an elevation of 100 m is 2.5 m/s.

    G. Location A; the wind speed at Location A at an elevation of 100 m is 11 m/s.

    H. Location B; the wind speed at Location B at an elevation of 100 m is 2.5 m/s.

    J. Location B; the wind speed at Location B at an elevation of 100 m is 11 m/s.

LEVEL 4: READING A GRAPH

Passage II

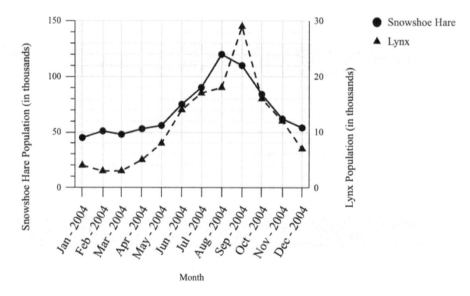

5. According to the figure, during what month of 2004 was the snowshoe hare population closest to 100,000?

    A. July

    B. August

    C. September

    D. December

6. According to the figure, which population had the highest peak in 2004?

    F. Snowshoe hare, because it had a peak population of 120,000.
    G. Snowshoe hare, because it had a peak population of 145,000.
    H. Lynx, because it had a peak population of 29,000.
    J. Lynx, because it had a peak population of 145,000.

7. In May 2004, compared with the lynx population, the snowshoe hare population was approximately:

    A. 7,000 lower
    B. 35,000 lower.
    C. 50,000 higher.
    D. 125,000 higher.

8. According to the figure, when was the size of the snowshoe hare population in 2004 closest to the size that the lynx population was in September 2004?

    F. January
    G. April
    H. August
    J. September

Answers

1. B	5. A
2. H	6. F
3. C	7. C
4. G	8. F

Full Solutions

2.

You first need to recognize that "ground level" means an elevation of 0 m, which occurs at the leftmost point of the x-axis. The answer can be found along the y-axis. The question asks for Location A, which is represented by the solid line with diamonds. Follow the y-axis (elevation = 0 m) until you hit the solid line with diamonds. The diamond is on the y-axis at 9 meters per second, choice **H**.

3.

If you look at the figure, you see that each point is 100 m away as marked along the x-axis. When the question says "for each 100 m increase in elevation", it means from point to point, left to right. "wind speed also increased" means the line goes up, because wind speed is labeled along the y-axis. You are looking to see if either line moves upward from point to point, left to right. Both lines (Location A and Location B) move upward from point to point, left to right, across every interval. Therefore, the answer is choice **C**.

4.

"Maximize wind exposure" means the highest wind speed. This is measured on the y-axis. The turbine will be 100 m high, so you want to see which location has a higher point at 100 m elevation. Follow the x-axis to 100 m, which is near the left. Follow the graph up to the higher point, which is a diamond on a solid line (Location A, according to the key). This point is at 11 meters per second. Thus, the highest wind speed at 100 m is 11 meters per second, at Location A. This is choice **G**.

5.

The snowshoe hare population is represented by the solid line with dark circles and the left y-axis. The line on the graph is closest to the 100 line (which means 100,000) when it is around 90,000, which corresponds to July 2004 on the x-axis. This is choice **D**.

6.

Although the line for the lynx (dashed line with dark triangles) reaches higher on the graph, the lynx axis (right y-axis) only goes up to 30,000. The line for the snowshoe hare (solid line with dark circles) has its highest point around 120,000 (left y-axis), which is choice **F**.

7.

In May 2004 on the x-axis, the snowshoe hare population (solid line with dark circles) was approximately 58,000 (left y-axis). In the same month, the lynx population (dashed line with dark triangles) was approximately 8,000 (right y-axis). Since $58,000 - 8,000 = 50,000$, the snowshoe hare population was around 50,000 higher, choice **C**.

8.

In September 2004 on the x-axis, the lynx population (dashed line with dark triangles) was around 29,000 (right y-axis). The snowshoe hare population (solid line with dark circles) never gets lower than 45,000 on the left y-axis, so it is closest in January 2004, at 45,000. The answer is choice **F**.

LESSON 6
SCIENCE CONTENT: SCIENCE MATH

You'll actually get about 2-3 "science math" questions on each test. What do we mean by "science math?" By this, we mean any math that is commonly seen in a high school science class and is less common in the math section. Some typical examples of these types of problems are questions involving percent error and interpreting formulas. Keep in mind that you are not allowed to use a calculator in this section, so "science math questions" will usually involve setting up calculations, but not actually carrying them out. If you do need to do calculations, they are pretty simple and involve round numbers like "80% of 1000".

How to Recognize

- Buzz words: percent, content, formula, multiply, divide
- The question will often ask you to take data and use it in a different way.

How to Attack

- Circle the graph name if it's mentioned in the question.
- Circle details in the question that tell you where to look on the graph (axis labels, values) and text (key words).
- Don't forget to consider the information in axis labels and graph keys.

What to Know

$$Percent\ Composition\ or\ Concentration = \frac{Part}{Whole} \times 100$$

For percent composition questions, look carefully to see whether you are being asked about percent by mass, percent by volume, etc. Concentration questions will often have the "Part" in grams and the "Whole" in liters or milliliters.

$$Percent\ Error = \frac{|Actual\ value - Experimental\ value|}{Actual\ value} \times 100$$

You should know the percent error formula. You won't see it on every test, but if you're looking for a 34+, then please have it memorized. The actual value can also be described as the accepted value. The experimental value is usually found in a table or graph. Don't forget that the denominator is the actual value—you might see an answer choice that has replaced the actual value in the denominator with experimental value.

You also might have to interpret a ratio. For example, if you are looking at an expression of the form $A = \frac{b}{c}$, you should know the following: as b increases, A increases; as c increases, A decreases; if b is greater than c, then A is greater than 1; and if c is greater than b, then A is less than 1. (Notice I used semicolons to separate "complicated" items in a list. The ACT throws this at you sometimes in the English section.)

Scientific notation is used as a shorter way to represent very large or very small numbers. Instead of writing out the number in standard form, the number is instead represented by a value multiplied by a power of 10. All you need to know is that the exponent tells you how many places you need to move the decimal point and in which direction to move it. A positive exponent means move the decimal point to the right and a negative exponent means move the decimal point to the left. For example,

5.0×10^7 means move the decimal 7 places to the right, so

$$5.0 \times 10^7 = 50{,}000{,}000.$$

5.0×10^{-7} means move the decimal 7 places to the left, so

$$5.0 \times 10^{-7} = 0.0000005.$$

You will also be expected to know a few common metric system prefixes, as described in the table on the following page.

Kilo-	x 1000
Deci-	x 1/10
Centi-	x 1/100
Milli-	x 1/1000
Micro-	x 1/1,000,000

For example, 8 kilograms = 8,000 grams. 8 milliliters = 0.008 liters.

The best way to attack unit conversions is to set up a ratio.

If a question is asking how many milligrams is in 34.1 grams, set up a ratio using the ratio in the table of 1000 milligrams in a gram.

$$\frac{1000 \text{ mg}}{1 \text{ g}} = \frac{x \text{ mg}}{34.1 \text{ g}}$$

Cross multiply to get

$$34,100 = x$$

There are 34,100 milligrams in 34.1 grams.

Try to answer the following question using this strategy. **Do not** check the solution until you have attempted this question yourself.

LEVEL 2: SCIENCE MATH

Passage I

Element	Percent by mass in glucose
carbon	40
oxygen	53
hydrogen	7

1. Based on the table, which element would most likely have the greatest mass in a 250 mg sample of glucose?

   A. Carbon
   B. Oxygen
   C. Hydrogen
   D. Phosphorus

Solution: According to the table, oxygen (middle row of data) has the highest percent mass (rightmost column) in glucose with a percent mass of 53%. "Percent by mass" means the percent of the total mass of the substance that is made up of the one component, which is oxygen in this question. Since oxygen has the highest percent by mass in glucose, oxygen will have the greatest mass in any size sample of glucose. This is choice **B**.

Try to answer the following questions using the math skills mentioned in this lesson. Questions 2-4 refer to Passage I above. Questions 5-8 refer to Passage II, which can be found after Question 4. The answers to these questions, followed by full solutions, are at the end of this lesson. **Do not** look at the answers until you have attempted these questions yourself. Please remember to mark off any problems you get wrong.

LEVEL 3: SCIENCE MATH

2. Suppose a 1.0 g sample of glucose had been collected. Based on the table, which mass of carbon, in would most likely have been present in the sample?

   F. 0.4 g
   G. 4 g
   H. 40 g
   J. 400 g

3. Based on the table, when a sample of 100 mg of glucose is placed in a test tube, which element accounted for more than 50 mg of the sample?

   A. Carbon
   B. Oxygen
   C. Hydrogen
   D. Phosphorus

4. Scientists measured exactly 0.025 kg of glucose. Which of the following values is equivalent to 0.025 kg?

F. 2.5×10^2 kg
G. 2.5×10^1 kg
H. 2.5×10^{-2} kg
J. 2.5×10^{-3} kg

LEVEL 4: SCIENCE MATH

Passage II

For each of four locations, temperature in degrees Celsius was measured at the soil surface and at a subsurface depth of 0.5 meters. Each surface temperature, S, was divided by subsurface temperature, F, and then multiplied by 100.

Site	$\dfrac{S}{F}\%$
Site A	10
Site B	18
Site C	15
Site D	14

5. If the temperature at the soil surface at Site A was 0.4°C, the soil at a subsurface depth of 0.5 meters was closest to which value?

A. 4°C
B. 10°C
C. 14°C
D. 40°C

6. Suppose the actual temperature at the soil surface at Site A was 4.5°C, although the scientists had recorded a soil surface temperature of 4.0°C. Which of the following expressions would give the percent error for the value of soil surface temperature at Site A?

F. $\dfrac{|4.5-4.0|}{4.5} \times 100\%$

G. $\dfrac{|4.5-4.0|}{4.0} \times 100\%$

H. $\dfrac{|100-4.5|}{4.5} \times 100\%$

J. $\dfrac{|100-4.5|}{4.0} \times 100\%$

LEVEL 5: SCIENCE MATH

7. How deep, in *millimeters* was the subsurface soil temperature measured?

A. 5×10^{-1} millimeters
B. 5 millimeters
C. 5×10^2 millimeters
D. 5×10^3 millimeters

8. Based on the results of the experiment, is the soil surface temperature greater than or less than the soil temperature at a subsurface depth of 0.5 meters?

F. Greater; each surface temperature, S, was greater than 100% of F.
G. Greater; each surface temperature, S, was less than 100% of F.
H. Less; each surface temperature, S, was greater than 100% of F.
J. Less; each surface temperature, S, was less than 100% of F.

Answers

1. B	5. A
2. F	6. F
3. B	7. C
4. H	8. J

Full Solutions

2.
According to the table, percent by mass of carbon (top row of data) is 40%. 40% of a 1.0 g sample of glucose is $0.40 \times 1.0 = 0.40$ g. The closest answer is 0.4 g, choice **F**.

3.
50 mg is 50% of 100 mg, which you can confirm with the calculation: $\frac{50 \text{ mg}}{100 \text{ mg}} \times 100\% = 50\%$. The only value on the table that is more than 50% is 53% (middle row of data), the percent by mas of oxygen. Since oxygen is 53% of 100 mg of glucose, it is more than 50 mg of that sample. Therefore, the answer is choice **B**.

4.

A negative exponent in scientific notation means that we should move the decimal point to the left (a positive exponent means that we should move the decimal point to the right). Thus, 2.5×10^{-2} means that we should move the decimal point two places to the left to get 0.025. The answer is choice **H**.

5.

According to the table, $\frac{S}{F}$ at Site A (top row of data) is 10%. From the text, S is surface temperature and F is the subsurface temperature, measured at a depth of 0.5 meters. If the soil surface temperature (S) is 0.4°C, then we have $\frac{0.4}{F} = 10\%$. Multiply each side of this equation by F to get $0.4 = 10\%F$. Now, divide each side of this last equation by 10% or 0.10 and we get $F = 4$. Therefore, the answer is choice **A**.

6.

Recall that the formula for percent error is

$$Percent\ error = \frac{|actual\ value - experimental\ value|}{actual\ value} \times 100.$$

We are given that the actual value is 4.5°C and the experimental value is 4.0°C. Plugging these values into the formula, we get $\frac{|4.5-4.0|}{4.5} \times 100\%$, which is choice **F**.

7.

According to the text, the subsurface temperature was measured at 0.5 meters. There are 1,000 millimeters in a meter, so the depth in millimeters is $1000 \times 0.5 = 500$ millimeters. Now convert to scientific notation. Remember that a negative exponent means that we should move the decimal point to the left and a positive exponent means that we should move the decimal point to the right. Since we need to move the decimal point 2 places to the right to get from 5 to 500, the answer is 5×10^2, choice **C**.

8.

In this question, the answer choices help explain the correct answer. If S were greater than F, then $\frac{S}{F}$ would always be greater than 1, which means **greater than 100%**. Since all values are less than 100%, S was always less than F. So, the answer is choice **J**.

LESSON 7
READING: ARGUMENTATION AND EVIDENCE

Argumentation and Evidence questions show up a few times per test and usually as the hardest question in a given passage. An Argumentation and Evidence question will provide a statement and ask which scientists or students would be most likely to agree or disagree with it. You will also have to decide whether statements or data support or undermine arguments. The trick is to figure out (i) whether you're looking for agreement or disagreement, and then (ii) if the particular individual is agreeing or disagreeing—without mixing any of that up.

How to Recognize

- Buzz words: which student, which scientist, agree, disagree, support, undermine
- The question will almost always refer to the name of the individual you should be considering.

How to Attack

- Circle the Student or Scientist number if it's mentioned in the question.
- Figure out whether you're looking for agreement/support or disagreement/undermining.
- Find the right data point or line in the text.

Don't Get Tricked

- When looking at a Conflicting Viewpoints passage, consider that each argument or discussion is most likely formatted the same way; if the answer is in the first line of one argument, it is probably in the first line of the other ones as well.
- If in doubt, eliminate answer choices that contradict themselves.

Try to answer the following question using this strategy. **Do not** check the solution until you have attempted this question yourself.

LEVEL 2: ARGUMENTATION AND EVIDENCE

Passage I

Historically, fossil fuels have been the primary source of energy for humans. However, the demand for energy is predicted to increase and the supply of fossil fuels is finite. In addition, the *combustion* (rapid chemical reaction in the presence of oxygen) of fossil fuels continues to have negative impacts on Earth's ecosystems.

Student 1

Although fossil fuels are abundant, they are nonrenewable. If humans keep burning fossil fuels at the current rate, the supply of accessible fossil fuels will be depleted in fifty years. Renewable energy sources, like solar power and wind power, are infinite. Fossil fuels are also extremely efficient, but renewable energy technology is constantly improving.

Fossil fuel plants are becoming more efficient and better at limiting pollution; however, fossil fuels will never be "clean." Pollution is contributing to the extinction of many species and the deaths of hundreds of thousands of children every year. Scientists must focus on making renewable energy sources more efficient and affordable, so no more harm is done by fossil fuel combustion.

Student 2

Although fossil fuels are abundant, they are nonrenewable. Humans are predicted to use up the supply of fossil fuels within the next 100 years, but fossil fuels will continue to be a significant source of energy in the next fifty years. Renewable energy sources are becoming increasingly more efficient and affordable. Solar, wind, and hydroelectric power are currently used across the globe to produce clean, renewable energy.

Pollution from fossil fuel combustion continues to be a problem. Scientists should study how to make pollution from fossil fuel combustion less harmful to the environment, as well as prioritize making renewable energy sources more affordable and efficient.

Student 3

Fossil fuels are abundant in many forms. The demand for fossil fuels continues to increase and will continue to do so in the next 100 years. Additionally, fossil fuel technology is constantly improving, which expands the amount of fossil fuels available. We don't expect to run out of fossil fuels in the near future. Fossil fuels are also extremely efficient—no renewable energy sources come close to providing the same energy output as fossil fuels, so we should not focus on renewable energy.

Although fossil fuel combustion can release harmful pollutants, as technology has improved over the last century, power plants have been better able to limit the amount of carbon dioxide and other pollutants that enter the atmosphere due to combustion, so are likely to reduce the harm caused by fossil fuels.

1. Which students, if any, would be most likely to agree that fossil fuels are currently abundant?

   A. Student 2
   B. Students 2 and 3 only
   C. Student 3 only
   D. Students 1, 2, and 3

Solution: Scan the first argument for the word "abundant". Student 1 says "fossil fuels are abundant" in the first sentence. All arguments are usually formatted the same way, so since the answer for Student 1 was in the first sentences, the answer for the other students will probably be in the first sentence as well. Students 2 and 3 also say, in the first sentence, "fossil fuels are abundant." Thus, all students would agree fossil fuels are currently abundant, and so, the answer is choice **D**.

Try to answer the following questions using the strategies in this lesson. The answers to these questions, followed by full solutions, are at the end of this lesson. **Do not** look at the answers until you have attempted these questions yourself. Please remember to mark off any problems you get wrong.

LEVEL 3: ARGUMENTATION AND EVIDENCE

2. Which students would agree that humans will deplete the supply of fossil fuels within the next 100 years?

   F. Student 1 only
   G. Student 2 only
   H. Students 1 and 2 only
   J. Students 1, 2, and 3

3. Student 1 would be most likely to agree that a priority for scientists should be:

   A. studying fossil fuel abundance.
   B. improving renewable energy technology.
   C. improving fossil fuel combustion.
   D. studying power plant technology.

LEVEL 4: ARGUMENTATION AND EVIDENCE

4. Which students, if any, would disagree with the statement "Power plant technology has not changed at all in the last 100 years"?

   F. Student 1 only
   G. Student 3 only
   H. Students 1 and 3 only
   J. None of the students

5. Which students would agree that combustion of fossil fuels will be a significant source of energy in fifty years from now?

   A. Student 1 only
   B. Student 2 only
   C. Students 2 and 3 only
   D. Students 1, 2, and 3

6. Which students, if any, would be most likely to agree with the statement, "Scientists should prioritize making renewable energy sources more efficient"?

   F. Student 1 only
   G. Students 1 and 2 only
   H. Students 1, 2, and 3
   J. None of the students

73

LEVEL 5: ARGUMENTATION AND EVIDENCE

7. Suppose it were confirmed that the number of pollution-related deaths does not change even with advanced pollution reduction systems in power plants. This finding would most likely undermine the argument of which of the students, if any?

    A. Student 1
    B. Student 2
    C. Student 3
    D. None of the students

8. Which student, if any, would agree that pollution from the combustion of fossil fuels is a problem?

    F. Student 1
    G. Student 2
    H. Students 1 and 2
    J. Students 1, 2, and 3

Answers

1. D	5. C
2. H	6. G
3. B	7. C
4. G	8. J

Full Solutions

2.

This question is a bit trickier because the students don't explicitly state the answer. Student 1 says "fossil fuels will be depleted in the next 50 years," which agrees with the statement in the question. Student 2 says fossil fuels will be used up "within the next 100 years," which agrees with the statement in the question. Student 3 says "We don't expect to run out of fossil fuels in the near future," which does *not* agree with the statement in the question. Only Students 1 and 2 agree with the statement in the question. Therefore, the answer is choice **H**.

3.

Scan Student 1's argument for the word "scientists." Towards the end of the argument, Student 1 states "Scientists must focus on making renewable energy sources more efficient and affordable," which is the same as improving renewable energy technology. Therefore, the answer is **B**.

4.

Scan the entire passage for "power plants." They are only mentioned by Student 3. Confirm the student would disagree: the student states "as technology has improved over the last century, power plants," suggesting that power plant technology *has* improved over the last century. Therefore, the answer is choice **G**.

5.

The question wants the Students who think fossil fuels *will* be important in 50 years. Skim the first argument. Student 1 says "fossil fuels will be depleted in 50 years" in the 2nd sentence of the argument, which disagrees with the statement in the question. Since Student 1 disagrees, we can eliminate choices A and D.

Next, look at the 2nd sentence of the other two arguments. Student 2 says "fossil fuels will continue to be a significant source of energy in the next fifty years," which is almost an exact agreement of the statement in the question. Student 3 says "The demand for fossil fuels continues to increase and will continue to do so in the next 100 years," which isn't a direct restatement but is an agreement with the statement in the question. Since only Students 2 and 3 agree, the answer is choice **C**.

If you're short on time and meticulous about eliminating answer choices as you go, you can even skip reading Student 2's argument. Once you've eliminated choices A and D, both remaining answer choices have Student 2, so all you need to do is determine if Student 3 agrees.

6.

The question wants to know who agrees that that scientists should prioritize making renewable energy more efficient. Skim Student 1's argument for "scientists." The last sentence of Student 1's argument is almost a direct restatement of the question: "Scientists must focus on making renewable energy sources more efficient." Student 1 agrees, so we can eliminate choice J.

Next, look at the last sentence of Student 2's argument. Although Student 2 mentions other goals for scientists, Student 2 also almost directly restates the opinion in the question: "Scientists should study how to make pollution from fossil fuel combustion less harmful to the environment, as well as prioritize making renewable energy sources more affordable and efficient." Student 2 agrees, so we can eliminate choice **F**.

Student 3 doesn't say anything helpful in the last sentence, so skim Student 3's argument for the word "scientists." Since "scientists" aren't mentioned, reread the entire argument in more detail. The most helpful statement is the last sentence of the first paragraph, which says, "Fossil fuels are also extremely efficient—no renewable energy sources come close to providing the same energy output as fossil fuels, so we should not focus on them." That is a disagreement with the opinion in the answer choice, so the answer is choice **G**.

7.

When a question asks if a statement or data will "undermine the argument," you need to see which student disagrees with the given statement or data. In this question, the statement is that advanced pollution reduction systems in power plants don't change the number of pollution-related deaths. In other words, improving power plant technology won't make fossil fuels safer. You might remember that Student 3 is the student who liked fossil fuels the most. The last sentence of Student 3's argument is: "Although fossil fuel combustion can release harmful pollutants, as technology has improved over the last century, power plants have been better able to limit the amount of carbon dioxide and other pollutants that enter the atmosphere due to combustion, so are likely to reduce the harm caused by fossil fuels." If the improved technology did *not* reduce the harm caused by fossil fuels, then Student 3's argument would be weakened. The answer is choice **C**.

You may also notice that the answer choices each list a single student, so only read until you find one student's argument that answers the question. This is helpful if you don't remember which students had which main ideas in their arguments.

8.

Student 1 says fossil fuels will never be "clean" and mentions problems from pollution. Student 2 says pollution continues to be a problem. Student 3 describes pollutants as "harmful." Thus, all students would agree that pollution from fossil fuels is a problem. This is choice **J**.

LESSON 8
DATA ANALYSIS: READING A FIGURE

While less common than graph or table questions, figure questions can be trickier because figures can be *anything*. A figure can be any kind of visual display that is not a graph or a table. Sometimes it's a slight tweak on a graph, and sometimes it's a picture of a bird. There's no way to predict what kind of figures you might see, so you should learn strategies that will work for any figure you encounter.

How to Recognize

- Buzz words: diagram, figure, based on
- The question will almost always refer to the name of the figure or diagram you should use or the axis labels on that figure

How to Attack

- Circle the figure or diagram name if it's mentioned in the question.
- Circle details in the question that tell you where to look on the figure.
- Go to the correct figure.
- Read any labels on the figure.
- Figure out where on the figure you need to look.

Don't Get Tricked

- Don't get intimidated if you don't immediately understand the entire figure. Find a word or detail that looks familiar and work outwards from it. You may not need to understand the whole thing.
- If all else fails, put aside your science brain and use common sense.

Try to answer the following question using this strategy. **Do not** check the solution until you have attempted this question yourself.

LEVEL 2: READING A FIGURE

Passage I

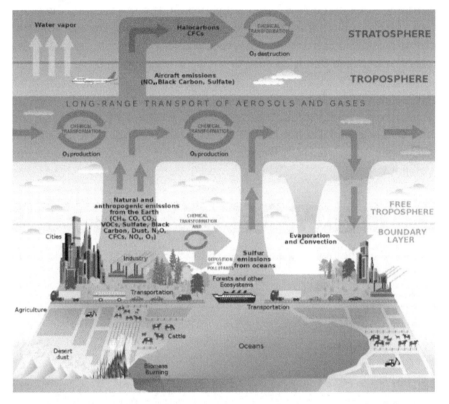

1. Based on the figure, which of the following is a type of pollution that is emitted from aircraft?

   A. O_3

   B. CO

   C. CO_2

   D. NO_x

Solution: Looking at the whole figure can be overwhelming, so use the question to figure out where on the figure to start. The question is asking about pollution from aircraft. Ignore the word "emitted" if you don't recognize it. Looking at the figure, you should see that there's a "ground" area and a "sky" area. Look around the sky area for the word "aircraft" or a picture of an airplane. Both are found in the upper left of the diagram. Aircraft emissions are "NOx, Black Carbon, Sulfate." The only one of those that is an answer choice is NOx, choice **D**.

Try to answer the following questions using the strategies in this lesson. The answers to these questions, followed by full solutions, are at the end of this lesson. **Do not** look at the answers until you have attempted these questions yourself. Please remember to mark off any problems you get wrong.

LEVEL 2: READING A FIGURE

2. Based on the figure, which of the following is NOT a type of pollutant created by Industry?

   F. NO_x
   G. CO
   H. Water vapor
   J. Black Carbon

LEVEL 3: READING A FIGURE

3. Based on the figure, in which layer of Earth's atmosphere are aircraft emissions a concern?

   A. Stratosphere
   B. Troposphere
   C. Boundary Layer
   D. Ground Level

4. In which layer of the atmosphere is O_3 destroyed?

   F. Stratosphere
   G. Troposphere
   H. Boundary Layer
   J. Ground Level

5. Based on the figure, where in Earth's atmosphere does long-range transport of aerosols and gases occur?

   A. Stratosphere
   B. Troposphere
   C. Boundary Layer
   D. Ground Level

6. Based on the figure, which type of pollutant is most likely to reach the stratosphere?

   F. CO
   G. CO_2
   H. CH_4
   J. CFCs

7. Based on the figure, which type of pollution do the oceans contribute to the atmosphere?

   A. Evaporation
   B. Sulfur
   C. Dust
   D. Black Carbon

LEVEL 4: READING A FIGURE

8. Based on the figure, which processes contribute to the cycling of pollutants up into Earth's atmosphere and back down towards its surface?

   F. Natural and anthropogenic emissions
   G. Evaporation and convection
   H. Aircraft emissions and chemical transformation
   J. Agriculture and chemical transformation

Answers

1. D	5. C
2. H	6. J
3. B	7. B
4. F	8. G

Full Solutions

2.

"Industry" is a label on the left side, just below the middle of the diagram. The large chunk of text above the "Industry" label lists all the "Natural and anthropogenic emissions," which means pollution that occurs naturally and that is made by humans. If you don't know those words, the arrows pointing upwards tell you that these chemicals are coming from Industry. The only one of the answer choices that doesn't show up in this list is water vapor, choice **H**.

3.

Ignore the word "emissions" if you don't recognize it. Looking at the figure, you should see that there's a "ground" area and a "sky" area. Look around the sky area for the word "aircraft" or a picture of an airplane. Both are found in the upper left of the diagram. You can see that the aircraft emissions are found in the same level as the "Troposphere" label on the far right of the diagram. This is choice **B**.

4.

Scan the figure for the words "O_3" and "destroyed." Near the middle of the top of the diagram, we see the label "O_3 destruction." This label is clearly in the "Stratosphere" according to the label on the top right corner of the diagram. Therefore, the answer is choice **F**.

5.

Scan the diagram for the key words in the question. Just below the "troposphere" label is the label "Long-range transport of aerosols and gases." Although this label is below the "troposphere" layer, it is definitely higher than the boundary layer. The answer is **B**.

6.

The topmost portion of the diagram is labeled "Stratosphere" on the upper right corner. The biggest arrow that goes into the stratosphere section is the one labeled "Halocarbons" and "CFCs." The only one of those in the answer choices is CFCs, choice **J**.

82

7.

The "Oceans" are represented by the body of water in the middle of the bottom of the diagram. In the middle of the diagram, there is an arrow rising from the oceans labeled "Sulfur emissions from oceans." The closest answer choice is "Sulfur". This is choice **B**.

8.

On the right-middle of the diagram, there is a section labeled "Evaporation and Convection." This label is in the middle of a big arrow going up into the atmosphere and then coming back down towards the ground. Therefore, the answer is choice **G**.

Note that it is helpful (but not necessary) to know that convection is the rising and sinking of a fluid, like air.

LESSON 9
READING: ADDITIONAL PRACTICE 1

This section provides an opportunity to practice the skills you've already learned by completing an entire reading-focused passage. The passage given here is a Conflicting Viewpoints passage, so you should expect to find many of the answers in the text. This is also a good opportunity to practice the passage strategies and reading strategies described in the Introduction.

Try to answer all of the following questions using the strategies in the previous lessons. Focus on your reading strategies, but some of the questions may be easier if you can understand the figure as well. The passage resembles one you might see on an ACT, with questions at all difficulty levels and getting progressively more difficult.

The answers to these questions, followed by full solutions, are at the end of this lesson. **Do not** look at the answers until you have attempted these questions yourself. Please remember to mark off any problems you get wrong.

LEVEL 1: READING

Passage I

A volcano is fueled by a *magma chamber* within Earth's crust. A magma chamber is a region of molten rock that has escaped the mantle. When the magma from the magma chamber reaches the surface, the volcano will erupt. Much of the data that scientists have on magma chambers comes from *seismic tomography*, which involves measuring the speed of seismic waves from earthquakes at dozens of seismic stations around the Earth. From this information, scientists can create three-dimensional images and infer the composition of features within Earth's crust. Although seismic tomography data can be helpful, scientists still do not have clear pictures of these features inside the Earth. Two scientists discuss the properties of magma chambers.

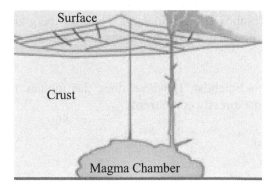

Scientist 1

Magma chambers tend to form 5-10 km beneath the surface of the Earth. These chambers are constantly fed from magma reservoirs, which are much larger and tend to form between 50 and 70 km below the surface. A series of dikes connect the magma reservoir below and magma chamber above. These dikes serve as passageways for the magma to travel upwards. Since the magma chambers are continuously filled from the reservoirs, magma chambers never empty out completely. They refill even as an eruption is occurring, even if the eruption continues for an unusually long period of time.

Although magma reservoirs are closer to the mantle, they are more solid than the magma chambers. A magma reservoir is normally less than 5% molten, whereas a magma chamber contains between 5-15% melt. The reservoir is large enough that even though it is mostly solid rock, there is enough magma to maintain the magma chamber. There may be more than one magma chamber supported by a single reservoir.

Scientist 2

Although many magma chambers form closer to the crust, those that contribute to the most violent volcanic eruptions are found much closer to the mantle at around 50-60 km beneath the surface of the Earth. These magma chambers are filled directly from the mantle by a series of dikes, which serve as passageways for the magma to travel upwards. When a volcano erupts, the magma chamber is completely emptied of molten rock, and then slowly refilled from the magma in the mantle. Magma chambers throughout Earth's crust refill at different rates, which can affect how much time passes between eruptions.

Magma chambers are nearly half molten rock. The rest of the chambers are composed of solid rock. The chambers are large enough that volcanic eruptions can be enormous and continue for an extended period of time.

1. According to Scientist 2, where does the molten rock in magma chambers most directly come from?

    A. Mantle
    B. Inner crust
    C. Reservoir
    D. Earth's surface

2. Which scientist, if either, discusses magma reservoirs?

    F. Scientist 1 only
    G. Scientist 2 only
    H. Both Scientists 1 and 2
    J. Neither Scientists 1 nor 2

LEVEL 2: READING

3. Seismic tomography measures waves created by:

    A. scientific experimentation
    B. earthquakes
    C. solid rock
    D. magma reservoirs

LEVEL 3: READING

4. According to Scientist 1, which usually has a higher proportion of molten rock, a magma chamber or magma reservoir?

    F. Magma chamber; the percent melt is usually greater than 5%
    G. Magma chamber; the percent melt is usually less than 5%
    H. Magma reservoir; the percent melt is usually greater than 5%
    J. Magma reservoir; the percent melt is usually less than 5%

5. According to Scientist 2, approximately what percent of rock in a magma chamber is molten?

   A. 0-5%
   B. 5-15%
   C. 15-40%
   D. 40-50%

LEVEL 4: READING

described by Scientist 1, the magma chambers described by Scientist 2 were approximately:

   F. 10 km lower
   G. 10 km higher
   H. 50 km lower
   J. 50 km higher

7. Do Scientist 1 and Scientist 2, respectively, mention the length of time between volcanic eruptions or the duration of volcanic eruptions?

	Scientist 1	Scientist 2
A.	Time between	Duration
B.	Time between	Time between
C.	Duration	Time between
D.	Duration	Duration

LEVEL 5: READING

8. Suppose seismic tomography showed that, immediately following a large volcanic eruption, the magma chamber beneath the volcano was completely empty of molten rock. This data would undermine the argument of which scientist, if either?

   F. Scientist 1 only
   G. Scientist 2 only
   H. Both Scientists 1 and 2
   J. Neither Scientists 1 nor 2

Answers

1. A	5. D
2. F	6. H
3. B	7. C
4. F	8. F

Full Solutions

1.

There's no easy shortcut to find this answer. Skim Scientist 1's argument for anything related to the question. In the second sentence, Scientist 1 says, "These magma chambers are filled directly from the mantle" so the correct answer is choice **A**.

2.

The word "reservoir" shows up several times in Scientist 1's argument, but zero times in Scientist 2's argument. The answer is Scientist 1 only, choice **F**.

3.

You might remember "seismic tomography" was mentioned in the first paragraph of the passage. If you don't, scan the passage for those words, which you'll find italicized in the first paragraph. Seismic tomography measures "seismic waves from earthquakes," so the answer is choice **B**.

4.

Scan Scientist 1's argument for numbers with percents. There are two: 5% and 5-15%. 5% refers to the reservoir and 5-15% refers to the magma chambers. The magma chambers have a greater proportion molten rock of more than 5%. This is choice **F**.

5.

You can scan Scientist 2's argument for numbers with percents, but there aren't any. Although it's tricky to find, once you find the right sentence, the answer is pretty clear. The first sentence of the second paragraph is "Magma chambers are nearly half molten rock." The best answer choice is 40-50%, choice **D**.

6.

Scan for the word "magma chamber" and any nearby numbers. In the first sentence of Scientist 1's argument, the text states magma chambers are "5-10 km beneath the surface." Next, look at the first sentence of Scientist 2's argument, which says magma chambers are "50-60 km beneath the surface." Reread the question to make sure you're looking at the scientists in the right order. The question is asking about Scientist 2, who says the chambers are about 50 km lower than Scientist 1 suggests. This is choice **H**.

Don't get mixed up about direction; the greater the depth, the lower the location.

7.

This question is tricky for two reasons: there are no easy key words to look for, and it's easy to mix up the scientists. Jot down notes to keep track. Beside each argument, write "time between" or "duration", which are the words in the answer choices. You can scan for words like "volcano" and "duration," but it won't really help you here. Scientist 1 says "even if the eruption continues for an unusually long period of time," which refers to the duration of a volcano. Since that information is in the last sentence of the first paragraph for Scientist 1, look in the last sentence of the first paragraph for Scientist 2. This sentence includes the words "which can affect how much time passes between eruptions." Scientist 1 talks about duration and Scientist 2 talks about time between eruptions. The answer is choice **C**.

8.

If you look at the answer choices, you'll notice that either one, both, or neither arguments can have the information, so you'll need to skim both arguments. The statement in the question is that after a volcanic eruption, the magma chamber is empty. Towards the end of Scientist 1's first paragraph is the statement "Since the magma chambers are continuously filled from the reservoirs, magma chambers never empty out completely." In the same place in Scientist 2's argument is the statement "When a volcano erupts, the magma chamber is almost completely emptied of molten rock." Since Scientist 1 states that magma chambers never empty out and Scientist 2 states they do empty completely, the statement in the question undermines the argument of Scientist 1 only. Therefore, the answer is choice **F**.

LESSON 10
DATA ANALYSIS: ADDITIONAL PRACTICE 1

This section provides an opportunity to practice the skills you've already learned by completing an entire data-focused passage. This is an experiment passage, but there is relatively little text. You should expect to find most of the answers in the figures.

The passage resembles one you might see on an ACT, with questions at all difficulty levels and getting progressively more difficult. The answers to these questions, followed by full solutions, are at the end of this lesson. **Do not** look at the answers until you have attempted these questions yourself. Please remember to mark off any problems you get wrong.

LEVEL 1: DATA ANALYSIS

Passage I

Water and wind are significant drivers of *weathering* (breakdown of rock) and occur with different frequencies at different elevations. Small relative particle size of soil can be evidence that a significant weathering has occurred. Scientists investigated the relationship between soil particle size and elevation at two different locations.

Experiment 1

Scientists collected a 1 cubic meter sample of soil from Location A and filtered the soil through progressively smaller sieves (see Table 1).

Table 1			
Sieve size (millimeters)	Particle size	% retained	% passing
40		0.0	100.0
35		0.0	100.0
30	coarse gravel	0.0	100.0
25		1.3	98.7
20		2.5	97.5
15	fine gravel	3.2	96.8
10		4.8	95.2

Experiment 2

Scientists collected a 1 cubic meter sample of soil from several elevations at Locations A and B. Figure 1 shows the average soil particle size of each sample.

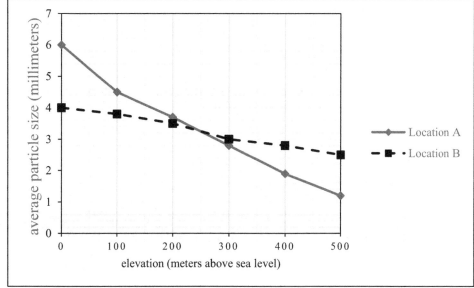

Figure 1

1. According to Table 1, what percent of the soil sample is retained when the sample is run through a 25 millimeter sieve?

   A. 0.0%
   B. 1.3%
   C. 98.7%
   D. 100.0%

2. According to Table 1, which size sieve retained the greatest percentage of particles?

   F. 10 millimeters
   G. 20 millimeters
   H. 25 millimeters
   J. 40 millimeters

LEVEL 2: DATA ANALYSIS

3. According to Figure 1, what is the average particle size in millimeters at Location B at an elevation of 400 meters above sea level?

   A. 1.9 millimeters
   B. 2.8 millimeters
   C. 4.0 millimeters
   D. 6.0 millimeters

4. At what elevation is the average particle size in millimeters the same at both Location A and Location B?

   F. 200 meters
   G. 250 meters
   H. 300 meters
   J. 350 meters

LEVEL 3: DATA ANALYSIS

5. What is the average particle size in millimeters at sea level at location A?

   A. 0 millimeters
   B. 2 millimeters
   C. 4 millimeters
   D. 6 millimeters

6. Which of the following is a possible particle size of fine gravel?

   F. 14 millimeters
   G. 21 millimeters
   H. 26 millimeters
   J. 31 millimeters

LEVEL 4: DATA ANALYSIS

7. Compared to the average particle size at an elevation of 500 meters at Location B, the average particle size at an elevation of 500 meters at Location A was:

A. 1.3 millimeters higher
B. 1.3 millimeters lower
C. 2.0 millimeters higher
D. 2.0 millimeters lower

8. In Experiment 1, the size of the largest particle in millimeters was most likely:

F. less than 20 millimeters
G. between 20 and 25 millimeters
H. between 25 and 30 millimeters
J. greater than 30 millimeters

Answers

1. B	5. D
2. F	6. F
3. B	7. B
4. G	8. H

Full Solutions

1.

Look at Table 1. The leftmost column is sieve size in millimeters, so look for 25. It's about halfway down. Follow the 25 line over to the second column from the right, which is percent retained. 1.3% is retained from the 25 millimeter sieve. This is choice **B**.

2.

Look at Table 1. Sieve size is the leftmost column and percent retained is the second column from the right. Go down the percent retained column to find the highest number. At the bottom of this column is 4.8%. Follow the bottom row of data to the left, where it lines up with a sieve size of 10 millimeters, which is choice **F**.

3.

Look at Figure 1, which has average particle size in millimeters on the y-axis (vertical axis) and elevation in meters above sea level on the x-axis (horizontal axis). The key on the right side of the graph shows Location B as a dashed line with squares. Look on the x-axis to find the 400 mark, which is right of the center. Follow the 400 line up to the square. Follow the graph over to the y-axis from that square. The square is around 3 millimeters. The closest answer is 2.8 millimeters, choice **B**.

4.

Elevation is only mentioned on Figure 1, so look there. The key shows that the lines are Location A and Location B and the y-axis (vertical axis) is average particle size. The two locations will have the same average particle size where the two lines meet. Find the point where they meet, which is near the middle of the graph, and follow the graph down to the x-axis (horizontal axis). The lines meet at the line between 200 meters and 300 meters, which is about 250 meters. The answer is choice **G**.

5.

The trick here is recognizing that "sea level" means 0 meters above sea level. Figure 1 has elevation on the x-axis (horizontal axis), so look where elevation is 0 meters, which is the far left corner. Follow the left edge of the graph up to the solid line with diamonds, which represents Location A. The diamond is at 6 millimeters, which is choice **D**.

6.

In Table 1, fine gravel is collected in 10 and 15 millimeter sieves. The only answer choice that falls within this range is 14 millimeters. Therefore, the answer is choice **F**.

7.

Elevation is on Figure 1, so look there. Elevation is the x-axis (horizontal axis). Follow the x-axis to find 500 meters, which is at the far right. Follow the 500 meter mark up, and see the diamond (Location A, according to the key) at around 1 millimeter average particle size and the square (Location B) around 2.5 millimeters. The two locations are around 1.5 millimeters apart, with Location B higher. Double check the question, which is asking about Location A. Location A is around 1.5 millimeters lower than Location B. The closest answer is choice **B**.

8.

This question is tricky because you need to understand what is going on in Table 1. The table shows how much of a soil sample was held by a sieve, which is a tool with holes in it used to filter particles of different sizes. Anything smaller than the holes will fall through and anything bigger than the holes will be retained. 1.3% of the remaining sample was retained in a sieve with 25 millimeter holes. No sample was retained in a sieve with 30 millimeter holes. That means the biggest particles must have been bigger than 25 millimeters, because they were retained in a sieve with 25 millimeter holes, but smaller than 30 millimeters, because they fell through 30 millimeter holes. The answer is choice **H**.

LESSON 11
SCIENCE CONTENT: ADDITIONAL PRACTICE 1

This section provides an opportunity to practice the skills you've already learned by completing an entire content-focused passage. This is an experiment passage, so you should expect to find many of the answers in the description of the experiment and in the figures. This section also provides a good opportunity to practice the passage strategies and reading strategies described in the Introduction.

The passage resembles one you might see on an ACT, with questions at all difficulty levels and getting progressively more difficult. The answers to these questions, followed by full solutions, are at the end of this lesson. **Do not** look at the answers until you have attempted these questions yourself. Please remember to mark off any problems you get wrong.

LEVEL 1: SCIENCE CONTENT

Passage I

Glaciers form when snow layers on top of itself year after year. Scientists can learn from ice cores, which are samples drilled from glaciers. These samples can be as big as 3 kilometers long, but only a few centimeters wide. The more snow falls in a year, the thicker the layers of the ice cores will be. Ice cores can also be examined for chemical composition so that scientists can infer characteristics of the atmosphere at the time the ice core was drilled.

Experiment 1

Ice core samples were separated into segments and the height of each layer was measured as follows:

1. Each ice core was separated into 1-meter segments and labeled with the depth at which it was found.
2. Each complete layer within a segment was measured and catalogued.

3. If a partial layer was found at the deeper end of the core, its height was added to the partial layer at the top of the deeper segment.

The table shows the average height of the layers in each 500-meter section of ice core.

Ice sample depth range (meters)	Average layer height (meters)
0-500	0.051
501-1000	0.109
1001-1500	0.215
1501-2000	0.118

Experiment 2

A 2 cm slice of each layer was analyzed. The slice was examined for the presence of volcanic dust.

1. In Experiment 1, which of the following was kept the same for each ice core segment?

   A. Length
   B. Depth
   C. Number of layers
   D. Average layer height

2. In Experiment 2, which of the following was measured or observed by the scientists?

   F. Number of layers
   G. Location of ice core
   H. Presence of volcanic dust
   J. Presence of glacial ice

LEVEL 2: SCIENCE CONTENT

3. What was a constant in Experiment 2?

   A. Number of layers
   B. Length of slice
   C. Presence of volcanic dust
   D. Age of glacier

LEVEL 3: SCIENCE CONTENT

4. In Experiment 1, what was the independent variable?

   F. Length of slice
   G. Temperature of segment
   H. Depth of segment
   J. Age of glacial ice

5. According to the table, what is the average layer height between 501 meters and 1000 meters?

   A. 1.09×10^2 meters
   B. 1.09×10^{-1} meters
   C. 1.18×10^{-2} meters
   D. 1.18×10^{-1} meters

6. According to the table, what is the average layer height between 1001 meters and 1500 meters?

   F. 2.15 centimeters
   G. 21.5 centimeters
   H. 215 centimeters
   J. 2150 centimeters

LEVEL 4: SCIENCE CONTENT

7. Suppose the actual average layer height between depths of 1501 meters and 2000 meters depth was 0.120 meters. Which of the following expressions would give the percent error for the value of soil surface temperature at Site A?

   A. $\dfrac{|0.120-0.118|}{0.120} \times 100\%$

   B. $\dfrac{|0.120-0.118|}{0.118} \times 100\%$

   C. $\dfrac{|0.120-0.071|}{0.120} \times 100\%$

   D. $\dfrac{|100-0.120|}{0.120} \times 100\%$

LEVEL 5: SCIENCE CONTENT

8. According to the data in the table, the total number of layers between 0 meters and 500 meters depth is approximately:

F. 100
G. 500
H. 1,000
J. 10,000

Answers

1. A		5. B	
2. H		6. G	
3. B		7. A	
4. H		8. H	

Full Solutions

1.

Look for the word "ice cores" in the description of Experiment 1. Step 1 of Experiment 1 states the samples were separated into 1-meter segments, which tells you that the length of the segment stayed the same, choice **A**.

2.

The description of Experiment 2 is short, so read it all. The word "examined" tells you what scientists were observing: presence of volcanic dust, choice **H**.

3.

A constant is something kept the same. Read the description of Experiment 2. The only thing mentioned that would stay the same is the "2 cm slice," so length of slice stayed constant, choice **B**.

4.

The independent variable is the variable that is intentionally changed by the scientist. In this case, the scientists were looking at ice core segments from different depths and measuring the height of each layer within a segment. The factor varied on purpose is the depth of the segment, which is choice **H**. The independent variable is often found in the leftmost data column in a table and along the x-axis of a graph.

5.

In the table, average layer height appears in the rightmost column and depth appears in the leftmost column. Follow the left column down to 501-1000, which is the second row of data. Follow the row over to the right. The average layer height is 0.109 meters. We must rewrite 0.109 in scientific notation to match the answer choices. A negative exponent means we should move the decimal point to the left (smaller). 0.109 in scientific notation is 1.09×10^{-1}, so the answer is choice **B**.

6.

In the table, average layer height appears in the rightmost column and depth appears in the leftmost column. Follow the left column down to 1001-1500, which is the second row of data from the bottom. Follow the row to the right. The average layer height is 0.215 meters. There are 100 centimeters in a meter, so the answer is 0.215 x 100 = 21.5 centimeters, choice **G**.

7.

In the table, average layer height appears in the rightmost column and depth appears in the leftmost column. Follow the left column down to 1501-2000, which is the bottom row of data. Follow the row to the right. The average layer height is 0.118 meters. The formula for percent error is

$$Percent\ error = \frac{|actual\ value - experimental\ value|}{actual\ value} \times 100.$$

According to the question, the actual value is 0.120. According to the table, the experimental value is 0.118. Plug those values into the formula and we get $\frac{|0.120 - 0.118|}{0.120} \times 100\%$, which is choice **A**.

8.

In the table, average layer height appears in the rightmost column and depth appears in the leftmost column. Follow the left column down to 0-500, which is the top row of data. Follow the row to the right. The average layer height is 0.051. We use the formula:

$$average\ height\ of\ a\ layer = \frac{total\ height\ of\ all\ layers}{total\ number\ of\ layers}.$$

Since the average layer height is 0.051, it follows that over 500 meters (500 meters − 0 meters), there are 1,000 layers, choice **H**.

LESSON 12
DATA ANALYSIS: DESCRIBING TRENDS

You will see at least one question about trends on the test. It is most likely that you will see two or three throughout the ACT Science section. These questions are not particularly difficult, but they are very easy to get backwards. A trend question will ask you to identify a pattern, usually in terms of an increase or decrease. Often, you will have to describe the relationship between two variables.

How to Recognize

- Buzz words: increase, decrease, what is the relationship between, varied, most quickly
- Answer choices often include the words "increase" and "decrease."

How to Attack

- Circle the graph name if it's mentioned in the question.
- Circle details in the question that tell you where to look on the graph (axis labels, values).
- Go to the right graph and find the right line, bar, or wedge.
- Decide whether the values are increasing or decreasing.

Don't Get Tricked

- Carefully read the key to make sure you're looking at the right line. Think to yourself "dotted line with black triangles," or whatever kind of line it is, so you don't get confused. Trace the line with your pencil.
- If there are many points, a graph can have outliers and still follow a trend.
- Sometimes values go in the direction opposite to what you think. For example, depth or amount remaining can have a value of 0 at the top, with numbers increasing down the y-axis.

Try to answer the following question using this strategy. **Do not** check the solution until you have attempted this question yourself.

LEVEL 1: DESCRIBING TRENDS

Passage I

Current (Amperes)	Potential Difference (Volts)	Resistance (Ohms)
0.31	2	6.45
0.58	4	6.90
0.92	6	6.52
1.17	8	6.84
1.46	10	6.85

1. According to the table, as current increased, potential difference:
   - **A.** increased only.
   - **B.** decreased only.
   - **C.** increased and then decreased.
   - **D.** did not show a pattern.

Solution: Look for current, which is in the leftmost column of the table. Look for an increase in current. It increases from the top to the bottom of the table. Potential difference is the middle column of the table. From the top to the bottom of the middle column, the numbers increase, so potential difference increases. From the top to the bottom of the table, both current and potential increase, so as current increased, potential difference increased only, choice **A**.

Try to answer the following questions using the strategies in this lesson. The answers to these questions, followed by full solutions, are at the end of this lesson. **Do not** look at the answers until you have attempted these questions yourself. Please remember to mark off any problems you get wrong.

LEVEL 1: DESCRIBING TRENDS

2. According to the table, as potential difference decreased from 10 V to 2 V, current:

    F. increased only.
    G. decreased only.
    H. increased and then decreased.
    J. did not show a pattern.

LEVEL 2: DESCRIBING TRENDS

3. According to the table, as potential difference increased, resistance:

    A. increased only.
    B. decreased only.
    C. increased and then decreased.
    D. did not show a pattern.

4. Which variable, if any, appeared to decrease as current decreased?

    F. Kinetic energy
    G. Resistance
    H. Potential difference
    J. None of the variables increased

LEVEL 3: DESCRIBING TRENDS

Passage II

The figure represents a scientist's predictions of world use of different types of fuel over a period of 30 years.

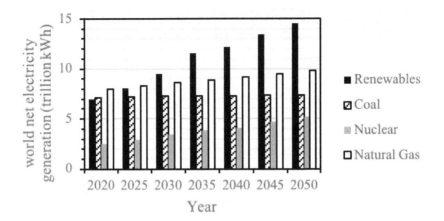

5. According to the predictions in the figure, as the amount of net renewable electricity generated increases, the amount of nuclear energy:

   A. increases only.
   B. decreases only
   C. increases and then decreases.
   D. increases and then decreases.

6. According to the figure, in terms of net electricity generated in the world, which type of energy is predicted to vary the *least* over the 30 years represented?

   F. Renewables
   G. Coal
   H. Nuclear
   J. Natural Gas

7. According to the scientists' predictions, from 2020 to 2050, the amount of energy generated will:

   A. increase for both natural gas and coal
   B. increase for natural gas and remain the same for coal
   C. remain the same for natural gas and increase for coal
   D. remain the same for both natural gas and coal

LEVEL 4: DESCRIBING TRENDS

8. Consider the predicted world net electricity generation using renewable energy sources from 2020 through 2050. During each five-year interval, the use of renewable energy:

    F. increases only.
    G. decreases only.
    H. increases and then decreases.
    J. decreases and then increases.

Answers

1. A	5. A
2. G	6. G
3. D	7. B
4. H	8. F

Full Solutions

2.

In the table, potential difference is the middle column. The middle column increases from top to bottom, so the question is asking about the table going from bottom to top. Current is the leftmost column. From bottom to top, the leftmost column decreases only, choice **G**.

3.

In the table, potential difference is in the middle column. The middle column increases from top to bottom. Resistance is in the rightmost column. From top to bottom, resistance doesn't show any pattern. The numbers increase, decrease, then increase again, but are all within a fairly small range. The answer is choice **D**.

4.

Current is in the leftmost column of the table. Current decreases from the bottom to the top. Scan the table for other columns that decrease from bottom to top. The middle one, potential difference decreases from bottom to top as well. Therefore, the answer is choice **H**.

5.

Renewable energy is represented by the dark bars. The bars get taller, which means the net world electricity generation in kWh increases, from left to right. Nuclear energy is represented by the solid gray bar. From left to right, the solid gray bars increase also. Thus, as renewables increase, nuclear increases, which is choice **A**.

6.

Predicted net electricity generated is measured on the y-axis. The bars that changed height the least, or stayed mostly the same, were the striped bars, which represent coal. This is choice **G**.

7.

The answer choices mention natural gas and coal. Natural gas is represented by white bars and coal is represented by striped bars. Time passes from 2020 to 2050 from left to right on the x-axis. From left to right, the white bars increase and the striped bars stay the same. Thus, from 2020 to 2050, generation of natural gas increases and generation of coal stays the same. The answer is choice **B**.

8.

Renewables are represented by the dark bars. From 2020 to 2050, which is the whole x-axis, the bars get taller and taller in relation to the y-axis, which is measuring world net energy generation. Since the bars increase in height during each interval, the answer is choice **F**.

LESSON 13
SCIENCE CONTENT: CELL BIOLOGY

Cell biology comes up quite a bit on the ACT, but almost everything you need to know appears in the text or on figures. You might need background knowledge in cell biology for 1-2 questions per test. However, having a basic understanding of certain concepts can help make passages easier to understand and make it easier to answer a few additional questions. You might even find some of this information helpful for navigating an occasional biology-focused English or Reading passage, although you should always look for evidence in the text to support your answer.

How to Recognize

- The passage involves a cell biology concept or experiment, but the answer to a question is not in the text or figures.

How to Attack

- Get as much information as you can from the text and figures.
- Quickly scan the passage for the answers to the question, but assume you will need background knowledge for 1-2 questions per passage.

What to Know

THE MITOCHONDRIA IS THE POWERHOUSE OF THE CELL. There isn't a whole lot more you need to know, except that "mitochondria" is the plural form of "mitochondrion," so it should really be "The *mitochondrion* is the powerhouse of the cell." This observation would better serve you on the English section of the ACT, actually.

The **cell** is the basic unit of all **organisms**, or living things. It contains **organelles**, which each have different functions within the cell. All cells have a **cell membrane**, which acts as a barrier that allows useful materials in and keeps harmful ones out, and a **nucleus**, which contains the genetic material of the cell and serves as the cell's control center.

"Genetic material" refers to **DNA** and **RNA**, which are long strands of **nucleic acids** (in fact, DNA is an abbreviation for deoxyribonucleic acid and RNA is an abbreviation for ribonucleic acid). Large chunks of DNA or RNA called **genes** act as blueprints for proteins that the cells create. DNA is a double-stranded molecule that looks like a twisted ladder. In animals and plants, DNA is **transcribed** (copied) into RNA, which is a single-stranded version of the same code. The RNA is then **translated** (converted) into **amino acids**, which are put together to form proteins.

Both **plant cells** and **animal cells** contain **mitochondria**, which act as the "powerhouse" by performing **cellular respiration.** Cellular respiration is the process of turning sugar in the form of **glucose** into usable energy, or **ATP**. The chemical reaction for cellular respiration can be simplified as:

$$O_2 \quad + \quad C_6H_{12}O_6 \quad \rightarrow \quad ATP \quad + \quad H_2O \quad + \quad CO_2$$
$$\text{(oxygen)} \quad \text{(glucose)} \quad \text{(energy)} \quad \text{(water)} \quad \text{(carbon dioxide)}$$

Plant cells also have a **cell wall**, which provides a rigid structure in addition to protection, as well as **chloroplasts**, the green organelles that contain **chlorophyll.** Chlorophyll allows plants to perform **photosynthesis**, which is the process of turning the energy from sunlight into sugar in the form of glucose. In other words, plant cells are turning light energy into chemical (stored) energy. The chemical reaction for photosynthesis can be simplified as:

$$\text{Light} \quad + \quad H_2O \quad + \quad CO_2 \quad \rightarrow \quad O_2 \quad + \quad C_6H_{12}O_6$$
$$\text{(energy)} \quad \text{(water)} \quad \text{(carbon dioxide)} \quad \text{(oxygen)} \quad \text{(glucose)}$$

Notice how cellular respiration and photosynthesis are nearly mirror images of each other.

Another way to classify cells is by their level of complexity (how complicated they are). **Prokaryotic** cells do not have organelles and the DNA or RNA just floats around in the middle. Prokaryotic cells include bacteria and archaea. A prokaryotic cell does *not* have a nucleus or mitochondria. The other kind of cells you might have to know is **eukaryotic** cells. Eukaryotic cells (pronounced "YOU-karyotic," so you can remember it's like YOU and ME) have organelles and often make up more complex organisms, like animals and plants. Eukaryotic cells also make up some simpler organisms like fungi (mushrooms, yeast) and protists.

When scientists study bacteria in a lab, they often grow the bacteria in growth medium or nutrient broth, which are different words for a substance that contains enough nutrition for bacteria to survive. Bacteria and other cells can also be grown on Petri dishes or plates, which are flat surfaces covered with a solid or gel growth medium. A growth medium can have antibiotics or different types of nutrients in it, which will only allow bacteria that are resistant to the antibiotic or able to metabolize the nutrient to grow. **Inoculation** is when bacteria or other cells are added to something.

Try to answer the following question using the information in this lesson. These questions are always considered more difficult than they actually are because the ACT assumes you have not freshened up your biology knowledge since freshman year. **Do not** check the solution until you have attempted this question yourself.

LEVEL 2: CELL BIOLOGY

1. In which organelle can most of a cell's DNA be found?

   A. Nucleus
   B. Cell membrane
   C. Mitochondria
   D. Chloroplast

Solution: The cell's DNA is stored in the nucleus (A). The cell membrane (B) serves as a barrier between the inside of the cell and the outside environment. Mitochondria (C) perform cellular respiration. Chloroplasts (D) perform photosynthesis. Although mitochondria and chloroplasts have DNA, it's only a small fraction of the cell's entire DNA. The answer is choice **A**.

Try to answer the following questions using the information in this lesson. The answers to these questions, followed by full solutions, are at the end of this lesson. **Do not** look at the answers until you have attempted these questions yourself. Please remember to mark off any problems you get wrong.

LEVEL 2: CELL BIOLOGY

2. Which of the following molecules is required for cellular respiration to occur?

   F. Water
   G. Sugar
   H. Carbon dioxide
   J. ATP

LEVEL 3: CELL BIOLOGY

3. Which type of cell does not have mitochondria?

   A. Plant
   B. Animal
   C. Eukaryotic
   D. Prokaryotic

4. Which organelle is not found in the cells of a bony fish?

   F. Nucleus
   G. Cell membrane
   H. Mitochondria
   J. Chloroplast

5. In which organelle do plant cells convert light energy to chemical energy?

   A. Nucleus
   B. Cell membrane
   C. Mitochondria
   D. Chloroplast

LEVEL 4: CELL BIOLOGY

Passage I

Scientists grew microbes under varying conditions. None of the test tubes initially had CO_2. The presence of CO_2 was observed to indicate whether organisms were present. The table shows which test tubes had CO_2 present at the end of the experiment.

Test Tube	Presence of CO_2
1	+
2	+
3	-
4	-
5	+

6. Which test tubes most likely have organisms present?

   F. Test tubes 1 and 2 only
   G. Test tubes 1, 2, and 5 only
   H. Test tubes 3 and 4 only
   J. Test tubes 1, 2, 3, 4, and 5

7. In which organelle does a chemical reaction occur to produce the dependent variable of this experiment?

   A. Nucleus
   B. Cell membrane
   C. Mitochondria
   D. Chloroplast

LEVEL 5: CELL BIOLOGY

8. In the experiment, why did the scientists most likely use CO_2 to indicate the presence of living organisms?

   F. All organisms perform cellular respiration, which produces CO_2.
   G. All organisms perform photosynthesis, which produces CO_2.
   H. Only some organisms perform cellular respiration, which produces CO_2.
   J. Only some organisms perform photosynthesis, which produces CO_2.

Answers

1. A	5. D
2. G	6. G
3. D	7. C
4. J	8. F

112

Full Solutions

2.

Cellular respiration is a process that breaks down sugar into ATP. The reaction requires sugar (G) and oxygen. It produces ATP (J), carbon dioxide (H), and water (F). The answer is choice **G**.

3.

Eukaryotes have organelles, but prokaryotes don't. Thus, prokaryotic cells do not have organelles such as mitochondria. The answer is choice **D**.

4.

Bony fish are animals. Animal cells do not have chloroplasts (J) or cell walls; only plant cells do. All eukaryotic cells, including plant and animal cells, have a nucleus (F), a cell membrane (G), and mitochondria (H). The answer is choice **J**.

5.

Photosynthesis is the process that converts light energy to sugar, which is a kind of chemical energy. Photosynthesis occurs in the chloroplast, choice **D**.

6.

The text states "The presence of CO_2 was recorded to indicate whether organisms were present." You should also know that living organisms perform cellular respiration, which produces CO_2. According to the table, CO_2 was present (right column) in Test Tube 1, 2, and 5 because those rows had a plus in the right column. Therefore, the answer is choice **G**.

7.

The text states "The presence of CO_2 was recorded to indicate whether organisms were present," which tells us that the presence of CO_2 was the measured, or dependent, variable (output). The dependent variable is often in the rightmost column or columns of a table. CO_2 is produced during cellular respiration, which occurs in the mitochondria, choice **(C)**.

8.

All organisms perform cellular respiration, which produces CO_2. Since the test tubes did not have CO_2 initially, the presence of CO_2 would mean that cellular respiration had occurred, which means there are living organisms in the tube. The answer is choice **F**.

LESSON 14
DATA ANALYSIS: CORRELATING

You will not see a correlation question on every ACT, but correlation shows up often enough that you should know how to attack it if you're aiming for a 34 or higher. These questions involve comparing more than one graph, usually line graphs, to decide whether they follow the same trend. This lesson has a lot in common with Lesson 12 (Data Analysis: Describing Trends).

How to Recognize

- Buzz words: correlate, in sync with, closer to

How to Attack

- Circle the graph name if it's mentioned in the question.
- Circle details in the question that tell you where to look on the graph (axis labels, values).
- Go to the right graph and find the right line, bar, or wedge.
- Figure out which lines or bars are most similar (they don't have to be exact).

Don't Get Tricked

- Answer choices will often include a description of a trend or relationship. Read it carefully and make sure they're not flipping it around!

Try to answer the following question using this strategy. **Do not** check the solution until you have attempted this question yourself.

LEVEL 2: CORRELATING

Passage I

A scientist observed two mutations in a population of wild-type bacteria *Streptococcus thermophilus*. The three different strains of *S. thermophilus* were each grown in a different flask of nutrient broth. Samples were collected every 4 hours for 24 hours.

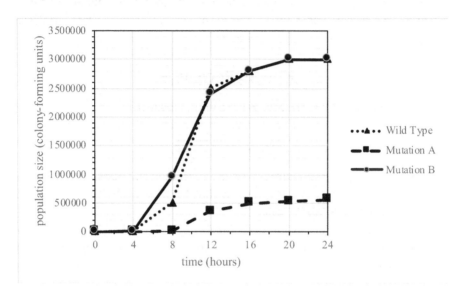

1. In the first 12 hours of the experiment, the population of wild-type *S. thermophilus*:

    A. increased at a rate most similarly to the rate of the population of *S. thermophilus* with Mutation A.

    B. increased at a rate most similarly to the rate of the population of *S. thermophilus* with Mutation B.

    C. decreased at a rate most similarly to the rate of the population of *S. thermophilus* with Mutation A.

    D. decreased at a rate most similarly to the rate of the population of *S. thermophilus* with Mutation B.

Solution: The x-axis (horizontal axis) shows time in hours and the y-axis (vertical axis) shows population size. The question is asking about the first 12 hours, so look on the left half of the graph, from 0 hours to 12 hours (along the x-axis). Scan the answer choices to see which lines we need to compare. The question wants to know which mutation changed at a rate most similarly to the rate of the wild-type. According to the key, wild-type is a dotted line with triangles, which is much closer to the solid line with circles (Mutation B) than to the dashed line with squares (Mutation A). Both lines are going up (increasing) over the first 12 hours at about the same steepness (rate). Thus, the wild-type increased at a rate most similar to the rate of increase for Mutation B. The answer is choice **B**.

Try to answer the following questions using the strategies in this lesson. The answers to these questions, followed by full solutions, are at the end of this lesson. **Do not** look at the answers until you have attempted these questions yourself. Please remember to mark off any problems you get wrong.

LEVEL 2: CORRELATING

2. According to the figure, as the population of *S. thermophilus* with Mutation A increased from hour 8 to hour 16, the population of *S. thermophilus* with Mutation B:

   F. increased more slowly.
   G. increased more quickly.
   H. decreased more slowly.
   J. decreased more quickly.

LEVEL 3: CORRELATING

3. Consider the growth of wild-type *S. thermophilus* from hour 0 to hour 24. Which mutated strain of *S. thermophilus* had a population growth rate over 24 hours that was most similar to the growth rate over 24 hours of the wild-type *S. thermophilus*?

   A. Mutation A; over that time interval, the Mutation A population grew faster than the Mutation B strain.

   B. Mutation A; over that time interval, the Mutation A population grew slower than the Mutation B strain.

   C. Mutation B; over that time interval, the Mutation A population grew faster than the Mutation B strain.

   D. Mutation B; over that time interval, the Mutation A population grew slower than the Mutation B strain.

4. Is the statement "Mutation A affected the population growth rate of wild-type *S. thermophilus* more than Mutation B" consistent with the figure?

   F. Yes, because the plot of Mutation A *S. thermophilus* more closely parallels the plot of wild-type *S. thermophilus*.

   G. Yes, because the plot of Mutation B *S. thermophilus* more closely parallels the plot of wild-type *S. thermophilus*.

   H. No, because the plot of Mutation A *S. thermophilus* more closely parallels the plot of wild-type *S. thermophilus*.

   J. No, because the plot of Mutation B *S. thermophilus* more closely parallels the plot of wild-type *S. thermophilus* .

Passage II

In a certain grassland region, *Buteo regalis*, the ferruginous hawk, preys on several species, including the black-tailed jackrabbit (*Lepus californicus*) and short-tailed shrew (*Blarina brevicauda*).

Study 1

Scientists used observational data to estimate the population size of *B. regalis* and *L. californicus* in September of every year from 1960 to 1970.

118

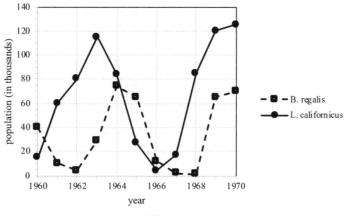

Figure 1

Study 2

A different set of scientists repeated Study 1 with *B. brevicauda*, during the same time interval.

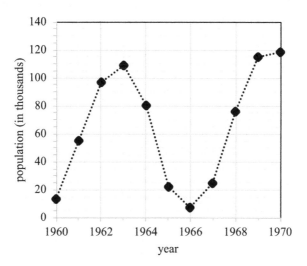

Figure 2

119

5. The table below lists the population of bull snakes (*Pituophis catenifer*) in the same ecosystem from 1960-1963.

Year	Population
1960	39,000
1961	8,000
1962	3,000
1963	32,000

Based on Figure 1, from 1960-1963, did the bull snake population more likely change in sync with the hawk or jackrabbit population?

A. Hawk; over that time interval, both the bull snake population and hawk population decreased and then increased.

B. Hawk; over that time interval, both the bull snake population and hawk population increased and then decreased.

C. Jackrabbit; over that time interval, both the bull snake population and jackrabbit population decreased and then increased.

D. Jackrabbit; over that time interval, both the bull snake population and jackrabbit population increased and then decreased.

6. Between 1964 and 1966, the grassland habitat experienced a drought, causing some populations to decline. Which organisms were most likely negatively affected by the drought?

    I. Ferruginous hawks
    II. Black-tailed jackrabbits
    III. Short-tailed shrews

F. I only
G. III only
H. I and III only
J. I, II, and III

120

LEVEL 4: CORRELATING

7. A scientist predicted that between 1960 and 1965, the short-tailed shrew population would increase during the same years as the ferruginous hawk population. Do the results shown in Figures 1 and 2 support this claim?

   A. No; the short-tailed shrew population increased between 1960 and 1963.

   B. No; the short-tailed shrew population increased between 1962 and 1964.

   C. Yes; the short-tailed shrew population increased between 1960 and 1963.

   D. Yes; the short-tailed shrew population increased between 1962 and 1964.

8. An indicator species is a plant or animal species that can be used to infer conditions in a particular habitat. According to Figures 1 and 2, which species would most likely be used as an indicator species for the *B. regalis* habitat?

   F. *L. californicus*; the population of *L. californicus* increased faster than the population of *B. regalis*

   G. *L. californicus*; the population of *L. californicus* changed more closely to the population of *B. regalis*

   H. *B. brevicauda;* the population of *B. brevicauda* increased faster than the population of *B. regalis*

   J. *B. brevicauda*; the population of *B. brevicauda* changed more closely to the population of *B. regalis.*

Answers

1. B	5. A
2. G	6. J
3. D	7. C
4. G	8. J

Full Solutions

2.

The x-axis (horizontal axis) shows time in hours and the y-axis (vertical axis) shows population size. The question is asking about hour 8 to hour 16, which is roughly the middle third of the graph from left to right. The question is asking you to compare the rate of increase or decrease of the Mutation A (dashed line with squares) population to the rate of increase or decrease of the Mutation B (solid line with circles) population. Both populations are increasing (going up), but Mutation A is increasing a little bit (shallow slope) while Mutation B is increasing a lot (steeper slope). Thus, Mutation B increased more quickly and the answer is choice **G**.

3.

Time 0 to 24 hours refers to the entire x-axis, so you are looking at the whole graph. The wild-type *S. thermophilus* growth curve is the dotted line with triangles. The other growth curve that follows almost the same path is the solid line with circles, which represents Mutation B. Mutation A, which is represented by the dashed line with squares, grew more slowly than Mutation B and wild-type. The answer is choice **D**.

4.

The wild-type *S. thermophilus* growth curve is the dotted line with triangles. The Mutation B growth curve, which is the solid line with circles, is very similar. The Mutation A growth curve, which is the dashed line with squares, was the most different from the wild-type growth curve. Thus, we can infer that Mutation A affected the growth rate of *S. thermophilus* more than Mutation B, choice **G**.

5.

According to the table, between 1960 and 1963 (left column), the bull snake population (right column) decreased from 1960-1962 and increased from 1962-1963. According to Figure 1, the hawk, *B. regalis* (dashed line with squares) also decreased from 1960-1962 and increased from 1962-1963. Therefore, the answer is choice **A**.

6.

1964-1966 is in the middle of both graphs, according to the x-axes (horizontal axes). In the middle of the graphs, all three populations are decreasing (slanting down), so you can infer the drought affected all of them, choice **J**.

7.

The population of the short-tailed shrew, *B. brevicauda*, is shown in Figure 2. The shrew population increased (went up in relation to the y-axis) between 1960 and 1963. In Figure 1, the hawk (*B. regalis*) population increased between 1960 and 1963 as well. Therefore, the answer is choice **C**.

8.

The question is asking which species' population was most similar to the *B. regalis* population. In Figure 2, we see that the population of *B. brevicauda* increased and decreased during the same intervals as the population of *B. regalis* (dashed line with squares) did in Figure 1. The answer is choice **J**.

LESSON 15
SCIENCE CONTENT: GENETICS

While some would argue that genetics falls within the field of cell biology (see Lesson 13), since there are a surprising number of ACT Science questions on this topic, we cover it separately in this lesson. A student who takes a handful of practice tests and one or two real tests will likely encounter more than one genetics passage. These passages can be especially tricky because you usually need some basic understanding of genetics to be able to answer some of the questions.

How to Recognize

- Buzz words: genotype, phenotype, probability, offspring, parent

How to Attack

- Get as much information as you can from the text and figures.
- Quickly scan the passage for the answers to the question, but assume you will need background knowledge for 1-2 questions per passage.

What to Know

The only genetics you are likely to see in ACT Science is classic Mendelian inheritance, but it is pretty important you know it well. This pattern of **inheritance** (passing to offspring, or children) doesn't work for all **traits** (characteristics), or even most of them, but is the model most likely to appear on the test.

A **gene** is a structure made up of DNA or RNA (see Lesson 13) that provides instructions for your cells to make a particular protein. DNA and RNA are made up of **nucleic acids**.

Recall from Lesson 13 (Science Content: Cell Biology) that the nucleus is the brain of the cell because it holds the DNA, which provides instructions for the cell to do everything it needs to do. DNA in the nucleus is usually stored as **chromosomes**, which are structures made up of neatly organized DNA strands and contain thousands of genes.

Since the nucleus contains two of each **chromosome**, there are two copies of almost every single gene. These two copies are called **alleles** and these alleles can be different from each other.

In Mendelian inheritance, some alleles are **dominant** and some are **recessive**. When one or both of an individual's two alleles are dominant, the dominant trait shows up. When both are recessive, the recessive trait shows up. For example, let's say we are looking at a gene that determines the color of a pea plant. G is the allele for green and g is the allele for yellow. The table below shows the possible **genotypes** (combinations of alleles) and **phenotypes** (displayed traits).

Genotype	Phenotype
GG	green
Gg	green
gg	yellow

A genotype that has two of the same allele is **homozygous** and a genotype with different alleles is **heterozygous**. Note that the dominant trait (green) has two possible genotypes: one homozygous (GG) and the other heterozygous (Gg). The recessive trait (yellow) only has one genotype, which is homozygous (gg). You also might see the prefixes "homo-" and "hetero-" elsewhere on the test. They mean "same" and "different," respectively.

When a parent creates a **gamete**, which is a sperm or egg in many organisms, the gamete has exactly half of the parent's genes. The offspring will inherit *one allele* from each parent, at random. You can calculate the odds of inheriting different alleles with a **Punnett square**.

125

In a Punnett square, the genotypes of the parents are displayed on the outside of the square and the four boxes inside the square show the possible offspring genotypes, each with equal probability. Let's continue with the above example of the color of a pea plant. The squares below show the different combinations we are likely to see:

Homozygous green (GG) parent mates with yellow (gg) parent. In this case, 100% (4/4) of the offspring are heterozygous green (Gg).

	G	G
g	Gg	Gg
g	Gg	Gg

Homozygous green (GG) parent mates with heterozygous green (Gg) parent. In this case, 100% (4/4) of the offspring are green, although half are homozygous (GG) and half are heterozygous (Gg).

	G	G
G	GG	GG
g	Gg	Gg

Heterozygous green (Gg) parent mates with heterozygous green (Gg) parent. In this case, 75% (3/4) of the offspring are green, although 1/4 are homozygous (GG) and 2/4 are heterozygous (Gg). The remaining 25% (1/4) of the offspring are yellow (gg).

	G	g
G	GG	Gg
g	Gg	gg

Heterozygous green (Gg) parent mates with yellow (gg) parent. 50% (2/4) of the offspring are heterozygous green (Gg) and 50% (2/4) of the offspring are yellow (gg).

	G	g
g	Gg	gg
g	Gg	gg

We can compare the probabilities of inheritance for two genes at the same time in a giant Punnett square, but we can get the same information just as easily by finding the probability for each gene separately, and then multiplying them together to get the probability for both. For example, if you are looking at the gene for color (G = green, dominant; g = yellow, recessive) and height (T = tall, dominant; t = short, recessive), and we want to mate two individuals that are heterozygous for both traits (GgTt x GgTt), you can make one big 4x4 Punnett Square, or look at two separate squares like this:

	G	g
G	GG	Gg
g	Gg	gg

	T	t
T	TT	Tt
t	Tt	tt

The probability of, say, a short green offspring is the probability of a green offspring multiplied by the probability of a short offspring. In the first Punnett square, the probability of a green offspring (Gg or GG) is 3/4. In the second Punnett square, the probability of a short offspring (tt) is 1/4. The probability of a short green offspring (Ggtt or GGtt) is 3/4 x 1/4 = 3/16.

Try to answer the following question using this information. First, try the question without referring back to the chapter. If you can't figure out the answer, look back at the information above, but **do not** check the solution until you have attempted this question yourself.

LEVEL 3: GENETICS

Passage I

The rabbit gene that codes for fur color has four *alleles*, or variations of the gene. The wild-type trait is brown fur, which is dominant over all the other fur types. Chinchilla, Himalayan, and albino fur alleles are all recessive to the brown fur allele. Chinchilla fur is dominant over Himalayan and albino fur. Himalayan is dominant over albino fur. Table 1 shows the different alleles.

Allele	Phenotype	Dominance
C	Brown	Dominant over all others
c^{ch}	Chinchilla	Dominant over Himalayan and Albino
c^h	Himalayan	Dominant over albino
c	Albino	Recessive to all others

1. What is the phenotype of a rabbit with one c^{ch} allele and one c^h allele?

   A. Brown
   B. Chinchilla
   C. Himalayan
   D. Albino

Solution: In this example, the phenotype is the fur color. According to the second and third rows of data in the table, chinchilla fur is dominant over Himalayan fur. A c^{ch} allele codes for chinchilla fur and a c^h allele codes for Himalayan fur. A rabbit with both a c^{ch} and c^h allele would have chinchilla fur because the dominant trait will appear. Therefore, the answer is choice **B**.

Try to answer the following questions using the strategies in this lesson. These questions are always considered more difficult than they actually are because the ACT assumes you have not freshened up your biology knowledge since freshman year. **Do not** look at the answers until you have attempted these questions yourself..

LEVEL 2: GENETICS

2. The gene for rabbit fur color is composed of:

   F. amino acids
   G. fatty acids
   H. nucleic acids
   J. monosaccharides

3. Where in a rabbit's cells would the gene for fur color most likely be found?

   A. Chloroplasts
   B. Cell membrane
   C. Mitochondria
   D. Nucleus

LEVEL 3: GENETICS

4. Which of the following genotypes could be a rabbit with chinchilla fur?

   F. Cc^{ch}
   G. Cc^c
   H. $c^{ch}c^{ch}$
   J. c^hc^h

5. What is the phenotype of a rabbit with the genotype c^hc?

   A. Brown
   B. Chinchilla
   C. Himalayan
   D. Albino

LEVEL 4: GENETICS

6. Suppose a rabbit with brown fur and a genotype of CC mated with a rabbit with Himalayan fur and a genotype of c^hc. What percent of offspring will have Himalayan fur?

   F. 0%
   G. 25%
   H. 50%
   J. 100%

7. What percent of offspring of a $c^{ch}c^{ch}$ rabbit and a Cc rabbit will have chinchilla fur?

   A. 0%
   B. 25%
   C. 50%
   D. 100%

LEVEL 5: GENETICS

8. Albino fur is associated with reduced fitness. Which cross is most likely to result in an offspring with reduced fitness?

F. CC x c^hc

G. CC x cc

H. c^hc x cc

J. c^hc x c^{ch}c

Answers

1. B	5. C
2. H	6. F
3. D	7. C
4. H	8. H

Full Solutions

2.

Genes are made of DNA, which is made of nucleic acids, choice **H**. Amino acids (choice F) make up proteins, fatty acids (choice G) make up lipids, and monosaccharides (choice J) make up carbohydrates.

3.

Genes are made of DNA, which is found in the nucleus, choice **D**. Although mitochondria contain some DNA, it is only a very small fraction of an individual's DNA.

4.

According to the second row of data in the table, chinchilla fur is represented by c^{ch}. $c^{ch}c^{ch}$ is homozygous (two of the same allele) for chinchilla fur, so will have a phenotype (apparent trait) of chinchilla fur. The answer is choice **H**.

5.

According to the bottom two rows of the table, c^h is Himalayan and is dominant over albino. The c allele is albino. An individual with c^hc would only have Himalayan fur, choice C, because the dominant trait appears.

130

6.

Make a Punnett square with CC and $c^h c$ parents.

	C	C
c^h	Cc^h	Cc^h
c	Cc	Cc

All offspring have a C allele, which produces brown fur according to the top row of data in the table in the passage. The table also tells you brown fur is dominant to all other types of fur, so if all offspring have a C allele, all offspring will be brown. 0% of offspring will be Himalayan, choice **F**.

7.

Make a Punnett square with $c^{ch}c^{ch}$ and Cc parents.

	c^{ch}	c^{ch}
C	Cc^{ch}	Cc^{ch}
c	$c^{ch}c$	$c^{ch}c$

50% of the offspring are Cc^{ch}, which is brown fur because C is brown and dominant over all other fur colors (according to the table in the passage). The other 50% will have chinchilla fur because c^{ch} is chinchilla, which is dominant over albino (according to the table in the passage). The answer is choice **C**.

8.

The question is asking for the cross with the highest probability of an albino offspring, which is cc because c is recessive to all other fur colors (according to the bottom row of the table). Choices F and G both have a homozygous (two of the same alleles) brown individual, which will *only* provide a brown allele to offspring. According to the first row of data in the table, brown is dominant over other fur colors, so all offspring of F and G crosses will have brown fur. For the other two crosses, make Punnett squares to find the probability of an offspring with albino fur, which is cc.

H:

	c^h	c
c	$c^h c$	cc
c	$c^h c$	cc

J:

	c^h	c
c^{ch}	$c^{ch}c^h$	$c^{ch}c$
c	$c^h c$	cc

The **H** cross has 2/4 or 50% of offspring that are cc and the **J** cross has 1/4 or 25% of offspring that are cc, so the answer is choice **H**.

LESSON 16
DATA ANALYSIS: EXTRAPOLATING

You will see at least one extrapolation question on every single test. Extrapolation is the act of predicting a data point by assuming a given trend will continue. Sometimes, you will be asked to interpolate instead, which means filling in a point between other data points.

How to Recognize

- Buzz words: suppose, if, would it have been, would be, most likely
- Answer choices often include intervals.

How to Attack

- Circle the graph name if it's mentioned in the question.
- Circle details in the question that tell you where to look on the graph (axis labels, values).
- Go to the correct graph and find the right line, bar, or wedge.
- If you're finding a value between two data points (interpolation), find the upper and lower limits for your answer and match them with an answer choice.
- If you're finding a value that is before or after all of the data points (extrapolation):
  - o decide whether the values are increasing or decreasing;
  - o find the next closest point or points;
  - o determine whether the value will be greater than or less than the value(s) of the next closest point(s).

Don't Get Tricked

- Don't spend too much time trying to figure out the exact value. The answer choices are usually very general and you only need to figure out which broad interval is correct.

Try to answer the following question using this strategy. **Do not** check the solution until you have attempted this question yourself.

LEVEL 2: EXTRAPOLATING

Passage I

Mass of Block (kg)	Force required to pull block at constant velocity (Newtons)			
	Desk	Carpet	Sandpaper	Tile
0.5	2.1	6.8	5.3	1.5
1.0	4.1	13.4	10.5	3.0
1.5	6.2	19.9	15.8	4.6
2.0	8.4	27.0	21.1	6.1

1. If an additional trial had been done with a 1.75 kg block on carpet, the force required to pull the block at a constant velocity would most likely have been:

    A. less than 6.2 Newtons.
    B. between 6.2 Newtons and 8.4 Newtons.
    C. between 19.9 Newtons and 27.0 Newtons.
    D. greater than 27.0 Newtons.

Solution: Although there was no 1.75 kg block, there were 1.5 kg and 2.0 kg blocks (leftmost column, bottom two rows). In the "Carpet" trial (middle column), the values seem to increase from the top to the bottom of the table. This trend matches the mass of block column (leftmost column), so we can assume that force increases as mass increases. On carpet, the 1.5 kg block required 19.9 Newtons and the 2.0 kg block required 27.0 Newtons. Since 1.75 kg is between 1.5 kg and 2.0 kg, and force increases as mass increases, the force required to pull 1.75 kg will likely be between 19.9 Newtons and 27.0 Newtons, choice **C**.

Try to answer the following questions using the strategies in this lesson. Questions 2-4 refer to Passage I above. Questions 5-8 refer to Passage II, which can be found after Question 4. The answers to these questions, followed by full solutions, are at the end of this lesson. **Do not** look at the answers until you have attempted these questions yourself. Please remember to mark off any problems you get wrong.

LEVEL 2: EXTRAPOLATING

2. According to the data in the table, how many Newtons would most likely be required to pull a 1.25 kg block across a tile surface?

F. Less than 1.5 Newtons
G. Between 1.5 Newtons and 3.0 Newtons
H. Between 3.0 Newtons and 4.6 Newtons
J. Greater than 4.6 Newtons

LEVEL 3: EXTRAPOLATING

3. Suppose a 2.5 kg block had been used instead. The force required to pull the block across a desk at a constant velocity would most likely have been:

A. less than 4.0 N
B. between 4.0 N and 6.0 Newtons
C. between 6.0 Newtons and 9.0 Newtons
D. greater than 9.0 Newtons

4. If a 0.25 kg block had been tested, would the force required to pull the block across the desk have more likely been greater than 2.1 Newtons or less than 2.1 Newtons?

F. Greater than 2.1 Newtons, because on a given surface, the force required to pull the block at a constant velocity increased as mass decreased.
G. Greater than 2.1 Newtons, because on a given surface, the force required to pull the block at a constant velocity increased as mass increased.
H. Less than 2.1 Newtons, because on a given surface, the force required to pull the block at a constant velocity increased as mass decreased.
J. Less than 2.1 Newtons, because on a given surface, the force required to pull the block at a constant velocity increased as mass increased.

135

Passage II

Students measured how much energy from a Wi-Fi transmitter was lost at different distances from the transmitter.

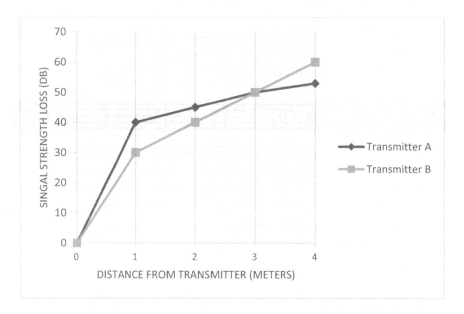

5. Suppose the signal strength loss had been measured at a distance of 0.5 meters from Transmitter A. What would the signal strength loss most likely have been?

   A. Less than 10 dB
   B. Between 10 dB and 30 dB
   C. Between 30 dB and 40 dB
   D. Greater than 40 dB

6. According to the data in the figure, which transmitter would likely have experienced greater signal strength loss by 6 meters?

   F. Transmitter A; the signal strength loss by Transmitter A was increasing faster than the signal strength loss by Transmitter B.
   G. Transmitter A; the signal strength loss by Transmitter A was increasing slower than the signal strength loss by Transmitter B.
   H. Transmitter B; the signal strength loss by Transmitter A was increasing faster than the signal strength loss by Transmitter B.
   J. Transmitter B; the signal strength loss by Transmitter A was increasing slower than the signal strength loss by Transmitter B.

LEVEL 4: EXTRAPOLATING

7. Suppose the students had measured the signal strength at a distance of 5 meters from Transmitter A. The signal strength loss would most likely have been:

A. less than 40 dB.
B. between 40 dB and 50 dB.
C. between 50 dB and 60 dB.
D. greater than 60 dB.

8. A student's desk was placed 1.6 meters away from Transmitter B. If Transmitter B created a signal that was 110 dB, the signal when it reached the student's desk would have most likely been closest to:

F. 35 dB.
G. 42 dB.
H. 68 dB.
J. 75 dB.

Answers

1. C	5. B
2. H	6. J
3. D	7. C
4. J	8. J

Full Solutions

2.
In the table, the tile floor is the rightmost column. A 1.25 kg block was never used, but a 1.0 block (second row of data from top) and 1.5 kg block (second row of data from bottom) were used. On tile, these blocks required 3.0 Newtons and 4.6 Newtons, so a 1.5 kg block would require a force between those numbers, choice **H**.

3.

The question is asking about the desk, which is the second column from the left on the table. The mass (left column) does not go up to 2.5, so we need to extrapolate. As mass increases (from top to bottom of the table), the number of Newtons increases in the desk column. The 2.0 kg block (bottom row) required 8.4 Newtons, so the answer will have to be more than 8.4 Newtons. Answer choices C and D both fit this description, so look back at the table. Each 0.5 kg increase corresponds with about a 2 Newton increase, so 2.5 kg will be about 2 Newtons more than 2.5 kg. A 2.5 Newton block would require about 10.4 Newtons of force, so the answer is choice **D**.

4.

According to the table, as mass increased from the top to the bottom of the table (leftmost column), force increased (any of the other columns). This also means that as mass decreased, force decreased. The 0.5 kg block (topmost row of data) required 2.1 Newtons to pull it across the desk (second column from the left, top number). Since force would decrease with less mass, the amount of force required to pull a 0.25 kg block across the table would likely be less than 2.1 Newtons. The answer is choice **J**.

5.

According to the x-axis of the graph, 0.5 meters was not a measured distance. Transmitter A (dark line with diamonds) was 0 dB at 0 meters and 40 dB at 1 meter, so the answer would be somewhere between 0 and 40 dB. More specifically, follow the 0.5 meter line, which is a light line halfway between 0 and 1 on the x-axis. The 0.5 meter line meets the Transmitter A line around 20 dB, which is between 10 dB and 30 dB, choice **B**.

6.

The x-axis (distance) only goes to 4 meters, so we will need to extrapolate beyond the graph. At the right side of the graph, the Transmitter B line (gray line with squares) is increasing faster than the Transmitter A line (dark line with diamonds). If the lines on the graph extend out to the right in the same pattern, Transmitter B will have a higher signal strength loss because the signal strength loss from Transmitter A was increasing slower than that from Transmitter B, choice **J**.

138

7.

The signal strength loss of Transmitter A was increasing at a somewhat steady rate after 2 meters. If it were to continue at the same rate to 5 meters, it would be higher than it is at 4 meters (52 dB) but still less than 60 dB. Therefore, the answer is choice **C**. This is one of the harder types of extrapolation questions you will see because you have to consider how fast the line is increasing, not only that it is increasing.

8.

At 1.6 meters away on the x-axis, Transmitter B (dashed line) will have lost around 35 dB. If Transmitter B originally created a signal that was 110 dB, but lost 35 dB, the signal that reached the desk at 1.6 meters would be 110 − 35 = 75 dB, choice **J**.

LESSON 17
SCIENCE CONTENT: PHYSICS

The ACT tests a wide variety of topics that fit under the umbrella of Physics: forces and motion, electricity, electromagnetism, and more. Like the other content areas, physics may only be required for 1-2 questions on the test, but will also be helpful for understanding some of the physics-related experiments.

How to Recognize

- Buzz words: force, gravity, normal, circuit, electromagnetic spectrum, visible light

How to Attack

- Get as much information as you can from the text and figures.
- Quickly scan the passage for the answers to the question, but assume you will need background knowledge for 1-2 questions per passage.
- If in doubt, lean on common sense.

What to Know

A **force** is a push or a pull, such as pushing a box across the floor or lifting a table up off the floor. When the force is applied along a surface, such as pushing a box across the floor, **friction** acts in the opposite direction. Gravity, or the **gravitational force**, pulls all objects towards each other. On Earth, the gravitational force pulls objects down towards the center of the Earth. The **normal force** acts opposite to the gravitational force when an object is on a surface. These different types of forces are shown in the figure below.

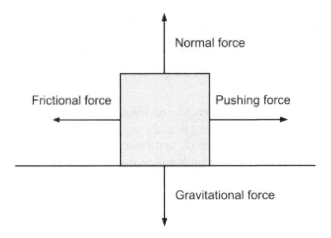

Velocity is the rate of change in position over time. It includes a direction, often represented by sign (a positive number represents motion in one direction and a negative number represents motion in the opposite direction). **Acceleration** is the rate of change of velocity over time. This is different than the everyday definition of acceleration, because it includes slowing down and changing direction in addition to speeding up.

Electricity is the movement of electrons through a closed **circuit**, which is a complete loop (or several loops) that contains a **conductor**. A conductor allows electricity or heat to pass through it, whereas an **insulator** restricts the flow of electricity or heat.

The **electromagnetic spectrum** describes different kinds of light waves organized by wavelength, although most of these waves are not visible to us. The spectrum ranges from very high energy waves like gamma rays to very low energy waves like radio waves. Visible light waves are in the middle of the spectrum and include a very narrow range of wavelengths. Longer wavelengths correspond with smaller frequencies and lower energy. Shorter wavelengths correspond with larger frequencies and higher energy.

Try to answer the following question using this information. First, try the question without referring back to the chapter. If you can't figure out the answer, look back at the information above, but **do not** check the solution until you have attempted this question yourself.

LEVEL 4: PHYSICS

1. Microwaves have a relatively long wavelength. They likely also have a relatively:

   A. small frequency; wavelength and frequency are directly related.
   B. small frequency; wavelength and frequency are indirectly related.
   C. large frequency; wavelength and frequency are directly related.
   D. large frequency; wavelength and frequency are indirectly related.

Solution: Microwaves are electromagnetic waves. With electromagnetic (and any other) waves, wavelength and frequency are indirectly related (as one increases, the other decreases). Thus, waves with a long wavelength will have a small frequency, choice **B**.

Try to answer the following questions using the strategies in this lesson. Content questions are always considered more difficult than they actually are because the ACT assumes you have not freshened up your physics knowledge since middle school. **Do not** check the solution until you have attempted this question yourself. Only questions 2 and 3 refer to the passage; the rest of the questions stand alone.

LEVEL 3: PHYSICS

Passage I

     The figure below shows the forces acting on a box as it is pushed across a tile floor.

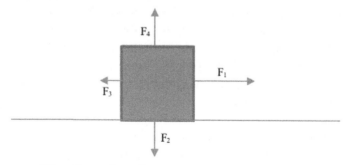

Direction of motion: ⟶

2. Which force displayed in the figure represents the normal force?

   F. F_1
   G. F_2
   H. F_3
   J. F_4

3. Which force displayed in the figure represents the force of friction?

   A. F_1
   B. F_2
   C. F_3
   D. F_4

4. Which of the forces below is most responsible for the Earth's relatively consistent orbit around the Sun?

   F. The gravitational force between the Earth and the Sun
   G. The gravitational force pulling downwards on the Earth
   H. The normal force pushing upwards from the Earth
   J. The strong nuclear force between the Earth and the Sun

LEVEL 4: PHYSICS

5. Which of the following is a good electrical insulator?

   A. Wood; wood allows electrical current to flow through it easily.
   B. Wood; wood does not allow electrical current to flow through it easily.
   C. Metal; metal allows electrical current to flow through it easily.
   D. Metal; metal does not allow electrical current to flow through it easily.

6. A closed electric circuit allows for which of the following?

   F. Continuous flow of electrons
   G. Continuous flow of protons
   H. Transport of neutrons
   J. Transport of hydrogen nuclei

7. Which of the following is NOT a type of electromagnetic radiation?

  A. Gamma rays
  B. Sound waves
  C. Visible light
  D. Radio waves

LEVEL 5: PHYSICS

8. Which of the following describes an object that is accelerating?

  I. A train gets faster as it leaves the station.
  II. A racecar maintains the same speed as it turns around a track.
  III. A bicyclist slows down while going up a steep hill.

  F. I only
  G. II only
  H. I and III only
  J. I, II, and III

Answers

1. B		5. B	
2. J		6. F	
3. C		7. B	
4. F		8. J	

Full Solutions

2.

The normal force acts opposite to an object's push against a surface. The box is pushing down on the floor due to gravity, so the normal force is acting upwards. The normal force is represented by F_4, choice **J**.

3.

Friction acts opposite to motion. According to the arrow at the bottom of the figure, motion is going towards the right, so friction would act towards the left. The answer is F_3, choice **C**.

4.

The major forces between planets are the gravitational forces pulling objects towards one another. The answer is choice **F**. Choice G is not correct because gravity does not act "downwards." It acts between objects.

5.

An insulator does not allow either heat, sound, or electricity to go through it. An electrical insulator would not allow electrical current to flow through it. Metals are good conductors of both heat and electricity, but wood, plastic, and rubber are good insulators. The answer is wood because it does **not** allow electrical current to flow through it easily, choice **B**.

6.

A closed circuit means a complete circuit. Electricity does not flow unless there is a complete loop. Electricity is the continuous flow of electrons, choice **F**.

7.

Gamma rays, visible light, and radio waves are all examples of electromagnetic waves. Sound waves are not; they are mechanical waves. Therefore, the answer is choice **B**.

8.

Acceleration is the rate of change of velocity. Acceleration includes speeding up, slowing down, and changing direction. I is speeding up. II is the tricky one; although the speed remains constant, the direction is changing, so acceleration is occurring. III is slowing down. Thus, all three are examples of acceleration. The answer is choice **J**.

LESSON 18
READING: ADDITIONAL PRACTICE 2

This lesson provides another opportunity to practice the skills you've already learned, by completing an entire reading-focused passage. The passage given here is a Conflicting Viewpoints passage, so you should expect to find many of the answers in the text. This is also a good opportunity to practice the passage strategies and reading strategies described in the Introduction.

Try to answer all of the questions using the strategies in the previous lessons. Focus on your reading strategies, but some of the questions may be easier if you can understand the figure as well. The passage resembles one you might see on an ACT, with questions at all difficulty levels and getting progressively more difficult.

The answers to these questions, followed by full solutions, are at the end of this lesson. **Do not** look at the answers until you have attempted these questions yourself. Please remember to mark off any problems you get wrong.

LEVEL 1: READING

Passage I

Demonstration

A science teacher moved a toy car back and forth on a linear track at a constant speed. The position of the car every second was graphed below. Three students were asked to describe the car's motion.

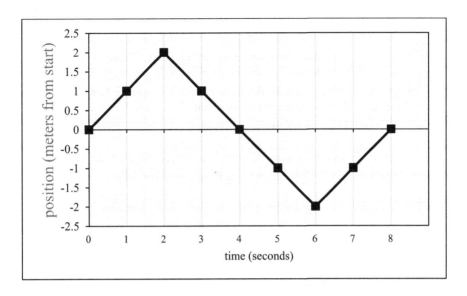

Student 1

The car's speed was constant but its velocity changed as it went around the course. Velocity is the rate of change of position. The velocity was positive when the car moved away from the start and negative when the car moved towards the start. Thus, the car's velocity was positive from 0-2 seconds, negative from 2-6 seconds, and positive from 6-8 seconds.

Velocity was never zero because the car's position was always changing. Velocity changed from positive to negative at 2 seconds and from negative to positive at 6 seconds, so the car accelerated at those times only.

Student 2

The car's speed was constant, so its velocity was constant. Velocity is the rate of change of distance. The velocity was positive the entire time because the car was constantly moving. Since velocity was constant, the acceleration was zero the entire time.

147

Student 3

The car's speed was constant but its velocity changed as it went around the course. Velocity is the rate of change in position. The velocity was positive when the graph showed a positive position and negative when the graph showed a negative position. Thus, the car's velocity was positive between 0 and 4 seconds and negative between 4 and 8 seconds.

The velocity was zero at 0, 4, and 8 seconds. Since the graph never shows a slope of 0, the car was accelerating the entire time.

1. Which student, if any, suggests the car's velocity remained constant?

   A. Student 1
   B. Student 2
   C. Student 3
   D. None of the students

2. Based on the description of the demonstration, which of the following stayed the same the entire time?

   F. Position
   G. Speed
   H. Velocity
   J. Acceleration

LEVEL 2: READING

3. According to Student 1's discussion, when was the car accelerating?

   A. At 2 seconds only
   B. At 2 and 6 seconds only
   C. Between 2 and 6 seconds only
   D. The entire time

4. Which student, if any, would most likely agree with the statement: "Velocity is the rate of change of position"?

   F. Student 1 only
   G. Student 2 only
   H. Students 1 and 3
   J. Students 1, 2, and 3

LEVEL 3: READING

5. According to the figure, the car passed the starting point at

   A. 2 seconds
   B. 3 seconds
   C. 4 seconds
   D. 6 seconds

6. According to Student 3's discussion, was the velocity of the car positive or negative when it was at a position of -1.5 meters?

   F. Positive; according to Student 3, the velocity is positive when the graph shows a positive position.
   G. Positive; according to Student 3, the velocity is positive when the graph shows a negative position.
   H. Negative; according to Student 3, the velocity is negative when the graph shows a positive position.
   J. Negative; according to Student 3, the velocity is negative when the graph shows a negative position.

LEVEL 4: READING

7. Suppose the car had continued traveling in the same direction at the same speed for another 1 second. Which student would most likely have said the car was accelerating from 8-9 seconds?

   A. Student 1 only
   B. Student 3 only
   C. Students 1 and 2
   D. Students 1, 2, and 3

LEVEL 5: READING

8. Which student's explanation is the most scientifically accurate?

   F. Student 1
   G. Student 2
   H. Student 3
   J. Students 1, 2, and 3 were all scientifically accurate

Answers

1. B	5. C
2. G	6. H
3. B	7. B
4. H	8. F

Full Solutions

1.

In the first sentence, Student 2 says "The car's speed was constant, so its velocity was constant," which directly states the velocity remained constant. Therefore, the answer is choice **B**.

2.

In the description of the demonstration at the beginning of the passage, the text states "at a constant speed," so speed stayed the same, choice **G**.

3.

In the last sentence of Student 1's discussion, the text states, "Velocity changed from positive to negative at 2 seconds and from negative to positive at 6 seconds, so the car accelerated at those times only." Thus, Student 1 claims the car accelerated at 2 and 6 seconds only, choice **B**.

4.

The students state their definitions of velocity in the second sentence of each discussion. Students 1 and 3 give a definition that matches the one in the question. Student 2 defines velocity as rate of change of distance, not position. Student 2's definition matches the definition of speed, not velocity. The answer is choice **H**.

5.

According to the figure, the car passed the starting point (distance of 0 meters from start according to y-axis) at 0 seconds, 4 seconds, and 8 seconds. The only one of those that matches an answer choice is 4 seconds, choice **C**.

6.

Student 3 states, "The velocity was positive when the graph showed a positive position and negative when the graph showed a negative position." When the position is -1.5 meters, which is a negative number, according to Student 3, the velocity would also be negative. The answer is choice **H**.

7.

This question is more about interpreting the students' discussions than about interpreting the graph. Student 1 says the car accelerates when it changes direction at 2 seconds and 6 seconds. If the car continues in the same directions at 8 seconds, it wouldn't accelerate, according to Student 1. Student 2 says the car is never accelerating and Student 3 says the car is always accelerating. Thus, only Student 3 would say the car is accelerating from 8-9 seconds because it is always accelerating. The answer is choice **B**.

8.

Velocity includes speed and direction, so when direction changes, velocity changes too. Acceleration is the rate of change in velocity, so when velocity changes, acceleration occurs. Only Student 1 has both of those definitions correct. Therefore, the answer is choice **F**.

LESSON 19
DATA ANALYSIS: ADDITIONAL PRACTICE 2

This section provides another opportunity to practice the skills you've already learned, by completing an entire data-focused passage. This is an experiment passage, but there is relatively little text. You should expect to find most of the answers in the figures.

The passage resembles one you might see on an ACT, with questions at all difficulty levels and getting progressively more difficult. The answers to these questions, followed by full solutions, are at the end of this lesson. **Do not** look at the answers until you have attempted these questions yourself. Please remember to mark off any problems you get wrong.

LEVEL 2: DATA ANALYSIS

Passage I

A *biodiversity index* is a measure of how varied the organisms in a region are. Biodiversity benefits ecosystems in a number of ways, including protecting ecosystems from climate variability and natural disasters.

The biodiversity index is calculated using the formula below.

$$\textbf{Biodiversity index} = \frac{\text{number of species in the area}}{\text{total number of individuals in the area}}$$

A scientist investigated the biodiversity index at 3 sites - Site A, Site B, and Site C - located at varying distances from a large archaeological field research station. At each site, the scientist marked off 3 plots that were each 10 meters by 10 meters on level terrain.

152

Site	Distance From Station (km)
A	5
B	15
C	50

Study 1

The scientist measured the biodiversity index at each plot and found the average biodiversity index for each site. Figure 1 shows the average biodiversity index for each of the three sites.

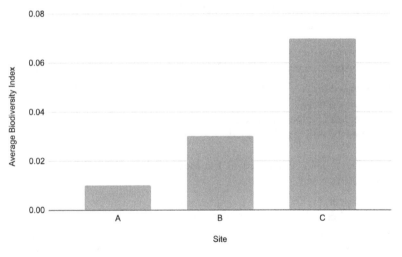

Figure 1

Study 2

After some time had passed, the scientist returned to the three sites to measure the biodiversity index twice a year for 5 years. Figure 2 shows, for each of the three sites, how the biodiversity index changed over time.

153

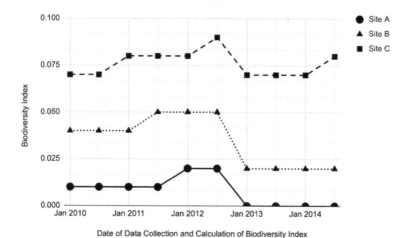

Figure 2

1. Based on the table and Figure 1, as the distance from the archaeological field research station increased from 5 km to 50 km, average biodiversity index:

   A. increased only.
   B. decreased only.
   C. increased and then decreased.
   D. decreased and then increased.

2. In January 2013, compared to the biodiversity at Site B, the biodiversity index at Site C was:

   F. 0.2 lower.
   G. 0.2 higher.
   H. 0.05 lower.
   J. 0.05 higher.

LEVEL 3: DATA ANALYSIS

3. Based on Figure 2, which site had the highest average biodiversity index across all the dates studied?

   A. Site A
   B. Site B
   C. Site C
   D. All sites had the same average biodiversity index.

154

4. Based on Figure 2, which of the following graphs best shows the biodiversity indices of Sites A, B, and C around July 2012?

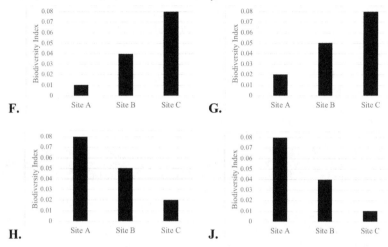

5. Some ecologists consider a diverse ecosystem to be one with a biodiversity index greater than 0.1. Based on Figure 1, on average, which sites would be considered diverse?

A. Site A only
B. Site C only
C. Sites A, B, and C
D. None of the sites

LEVEL 4: DATA ANALYSIS

6. Suppose that an additional site had been tested that was located within the archaeological field research station perimeter. Based on the results of Study 1, the average biodiversity index at that site would most likely have been:

F. less than 0.01.
G. between 0.01 and 0.03.
H. between 0.03 and 0.07.
J. greater than 0.07.

155

7. According to Table 1 and Figure 1, the scientists saw the most biodiversity at the site:

    A. farthest from the archaeological field research station, because as distance from the station increased, biodiversity index decreased.

    B. farthest from the archaeological field research station, because as distance from the station increased, biodiversity index increased.

    C. closest to the archaeological field research station, because as distance from the station increased, biodiversity index decreased.

    D. closest to the archaeological field research station, because as distance from the station increased, biodiversity index increased.

LEVEL 5: DATA ANALYSIS

8. A hurricane in 2012 caused a lot of damage to the region and had a detrimental effect on local flora and fauna. The scientist hypothesized that a higher biodiversity index would be protective against natural disasters. Do the experimental results support the scientist's hypothesis?

    F. Yes; Site C had the same biodiversity index in July 2014 and January 2012.

    G. Yes; Site A had the same biodiversity index in July 2014 and January 2012.

    H. No; Site B had the same biodiversity index in January 2010 and January 2011.

    J. No; Site A had the same biodiversity index in January 2013 and July 2014

Answers

1. A	5. D
2. F	6. F
3. C	7. B
4. G	8. F

Full Solutions

1.

According to the table, distance (right column) increased from Site A to Site B to Site C (left column). In Figure 1, average biodiversity index (*y*-axis) increased from Site A to Site B to Site C (*x*-axis). Thus, as distance increases, average biodiversity index increases, choice **A**.

2.

According to Figure 2, in January 2013, Site B (dotted line with triangles) was 0.02 and Site C (dashed line with squares) was 0.07. Thus, Site C was 0.05 higher than Site B. The answer is choice **F**.

3.

In Figure 2, the Site C line (dashed line with squares) was higher than the other lines at every date. Therefore, the answer is choice **C**.

4.

In Figure 2, at July 2012 on the x-axis, Site A (solid line with dots) is 0.02, Site B (dotted line with triangles) is 0.05, and Site C (dashed line with squares) is 0.08. The biodiversity index increases from Site A to Site B to Site C, which is the same order as the sites on the x-axes in the answer choices, so the decreasing graphs (H and J) can be eliminated. Only choice G shows Site A at 0.02 on the y-axis. Therefore, the answer is choice **G**.

5.

In Figure 1, the highest average biodiversity index (y-axis) is 0.07, so none of the sites is over 0.1. Therefore, none of the sites would be considered diverse and the answer is choice **D**.

6.

Within the field station perimeter means the distance from the field station is 0 km, which would be lower than all of the Sites. According to Figure 1 and the table, as distance increased, average biodiversity index increased. Thus, a smaller distance would have a lower average biodiversity index than the closest site, which is Site A, at 0.01. The answer is choice **F**.

7.

According to Figure 1, Site C (x-axis) has the highest average biodiversity index (tallest bar). According to the table, Site C (left column) is the farthest away (right column) from the research station. According to the table, distance (right column) increased from Site A to Site B to Site C (left column). In Figure 1, average biodiversity index (y-axis) increased from Site A to Site B to Site C (x-axis). Thus, as distance increases, average biodiversity index increases. The answer is choice **B**.

157

8.

Between July 2012 and January 2013, the biodiversity index at all of the sites decreased. We can infer that this was from the hurricane in 2012. Only Site C (dashed line with squares) had a biodiversity index that returned to its previous level. Site C had the same biodiversity index before (January 2012) and after (July 2014) the hurricane. Both other sites never returned to the same level biodiversity index. The answer is choice **F**.

LESSON 20
SCIENCE CONTENT: ADDITIONAL PRACTICE 2

This section provides another opportunity to practice the skills you've already learned by completing an entire content-focused passage. This is an experiment passage, so you should expect to find many of the answers in the description of the experiment and figures. This section also provides a good opportunity to practice the passage strategies and reading strategies described in the Introduction.

The passage resembles one you might see on an ACT, with questions at all difficulty levels and getting progressively more difficult. The answers to these questions, followed by full solutions, are at the end of this lesson. **Do not** look at the answers until you have attempted these questions yourself. Please remember to mark off any problems you get wrong.

LEVEL 1: SCIENCE CONTENT

Passage I

Transpiration is the release of water into the atmosphere from plants. Water is released through the stoma on plants' leaves. Using plants of the species *Arabidopsis thaliana*, students studied the effects of different factors on the rate of transpiration.

Experiment 1

Ten identical graduated cylinders were each filled with 60 mL water. One individual *A. thaliana* plant of uniform height and age was suspended in each cylinder. The top of the cylinder was covered with a plastic film with a hole cut into it for the plant's stem, as shown in the figure below.

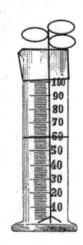

Figure 1

Five plants were put in a sunny location and five plants were put in the dark. Both locations were kept at 22°C. The height of the water was measured every 15 minutes for one hour. The average water levels for plants in each condition at each time were calculated. Results were calculated in Table 1.

Table 1		
Time (minutes)	Water level (millimeters)	
	Dark	Light
0	60.0	60.0
15	60.0	59.4
30	60.0	58.8
45	60.0	58.3
60	60.0	57.9

Experiment 2

Experiment 1 was repeated using only the plants in the light, except the students put a fan near the plants and turned it on. The average water levels for plants at each time were calculated. The results are shown in Table 2.

Table 2	
Time (minutes)	Water level (millimeters) Light + Fan
0	59.1
15	58.3
30	57.4
45	56.6
60	56.7

1. Which of the following is a product of cellular respiration?

   A. Carbon dioxide
   B. Oxygen
   C. Glucose
   D. Sunlight

LEVEL 2: SCIENCE CONTENT

2. Which of the following organelles performs photosynthesis?

   F. Mitochondria
   G. Golgi bodies
   H. Nucleus
   J. Chloroplast

3. According to the data in Table 1, from 0 minutes to 60 minutes, the water level of the plants in the light:

    A. increased only.
    B. decreased only.
    C. increased, then decreased.
    D. neither increased nor decreased.

LEVEL 3: SCIENCE CONTENT

4. Which of the following was an independent variable in Experiment 1?

    F. Presence or absence of fan
    G. Presence or absence of light
    H. Number of plants
    J. Volume of water

5. Compared to the volume of water remaining in light, the volume of water remaining without light:

    A. was greater at every time point after 0 seconds.
    B. was greater at some of the time points.
    C. was the same at every time point.
    D. was less at every time point after 0 seconds.

LEVEL 4: SCIENCE CONTENT

6. Compared to the volume of water lost to transpiration in light, the volume of water lost to transpiration in light with the presence of a fan:

    F. was greater at every time point after 0 seconds.
    G. was greater at most of the time points.
    H. was the same at every time point.
    J. was less at every time point after 0 seconds.

LEVEL 5: SCIENCE CONTENT

7. A student hypothesized that more transpiration would occur when photosynthesis was occurring. Do the results of the experiments support this hypothesis?

    A. Yes; light is required for photosynthesis and more transpiration occurred when the light was on.

    B. Yes; light is required for photosynthesis and more transpiration occurred when the light was off.

    C. No; light is required for photosynthesis and more transpiration occurred when the light was on.

    D. No; light is required for photosynthesis and more transpiration occurred when the light was off.

8. What is the most likely reason that the students cover the graduated cylinder in plastic film?

    F. To prevent photosynthesis from occurring

    G. To prevent cellular respiration from occurring

    H. So water wouldn't be lost through evaporation

    J. So light would not reach the roots of the plant

Answers

1. A	5. A
2. J	6. F
3. B	7. A
4. G	8. H

Full Solutions

1.

Cellular respiration is the breakdown of sugar to create energy. Glucose and oxygen are the inputs and carbon dioxide, water, and ATP (energy) are the outputs. So, the answer is carbon dioxide, choice **A**.

2.

Photosynthesis occurs in the chloroplasts, which is choice **J**. Mitochondria (choice F) perform cellular respiration. Golgi bodies (choice G) are involved in transport of materials within the cell. The nucleus (choice H) is the brain of the cell and stores DNA.

163

3.

According to Table 1, the water level in the light is the rightmost column. The time goes from 0 minutes to 60 minutes from top to bottom of the table. From top to bottom, the rightmost column decreased only. The answer is choice **B**.

4.

An independent variable is a variable the scientist manipulates on purpose and is different between experimental groups. In Table 1, which shows the results of Experiment 1, the two groups being compared are the light and dark groups, so the independent variable is the presence or absence of light. Thus, the answer is choice **G**.

5.

Table 1 compares the volume remaining with light (rightmost column) to the volume remaining without light (middle column). Read the question carefully so we see which way the comparison is going. The volume of water without light is greater at every point after 0 seconds, so the answer is choice **A**.

6.

This question is tricky because it's asking about volume lost, not volume remaining. According to Tables 1 and 2, the volume remaining in light (Table 1, rightmost column) is greater than the volume remaining in the light with the fan (Table 2, rightmost column) at every point after 0 seconds, so the volume lost is greater for the plants with light and fan. Therefore, the answer is choice **F**.

7.

Photosynthesis requires light, so photosynthesis is happening when there is light and not in the dark. In Table 1, which shows the results of Experiment 1, there is less water remaining in the light (rightmost column) than in the dark (middle column). Since more water lost means more transpiration, there is more transpiration when photosynthesis is occurring, which matches the hypothesis. The answer is choice **A**.

8.

For the scientists to accurately measure the water lost via transpiration, they need to eliminate the variable of water lost to evaporation. One way to do this is to cover the graduated cylinder with plastic film so that the only water lost is from the leaves. Thus, the answer is choice **H**. If you are unfamiliar with transpiration, you'll need to use common sense to answer this question.

LESSON 21
DATA ANALYSIS: INFERRING FROM DATA

Inferring from Data questions are considered by many to be the most difficult questions in the science section. They often show up as the last question in a passage. These questions usually ask you to use the data to make an inference (prediction, guess) or give you a hypothesis and ask you whether the experimental data support it. You will probably see between one and three of these questions on every test.

How to Recognize

- Buzz words: suppose, hypothesized, probably

How to Attack

- Circle the graph name if it's mentioned in the question.
- Figure out which data or trends will be needed to answer the question.
- Jot down notes, even if it's as simple as "A inc. as B dec."

Don't Get Tricked

- It's easy to flip trends and answers. Make sure you read carefully to figure out which value is being used as a reference and which value is being compared.

Try to answer the following question using this strategy. **Do not** check the solution until you have attempted this question yourself.

LEVEL 2: INFERRING FROM DATA

Passage I

Scientists measured the mass and volume of six different samples of plastic. The data were then used to calculate the density of each sample.

Sample	Mass (g)	Volume (cm^3)	Density (g/cm^3)
1	5.0	4.17	1.20
2	10.0	8.34	1.20
3	15.0	12.51	1.20
4	10.0	10.75	0.93
5	15.0	16.13	0.93
6	10.0	9.26	1.08

1. Different samples of the same substance have the same density. Which two samples are most likely the same type of plastic?

   A. Samples 1 and 4
   B. Samples 3 and 4
   C. Samples 4 and 5
   D. Samples 2 and 6

Solution: According to the table, Samples 4 and 5 both have a density (right column) of 0.93 g/cm^3. Since samples with the same density are the same substance, Samples 4 and 5 are likely the same substance. Thus, the answer is choice **C**.

Try to answer the following questions using the strategies in this lesson. Questions 2-4 refer to Passage I above. Questions 5-8 refer to Passage II, which can be found after Question 4. The answers to these questions, followed by full solutions, are at the end of this lesson. **Do not** look at the answers until you have attempted these questions yourself. Please remember to mark off any problems you get wrong.

LEVEL 2: INFERRING FROM DATA

2. Low-density polyethylene (LDPE) has a density between 0.917 g/cm^3 and 0.940 g/cm^3. Which sample is most likely LDPE?

   F. Sample 2, because its density falls within the given range.
   G. Sample 2, because its density is greater than the given range.
   H. Sample 5, because its density falls within the given range.
   J. Sample 5, because its density is greater than the given range.

LEVEL 3: INFERRING FROM DATA

3. Scientists determined that Samples 1, 2, and 3 are polyvinyl chloride (PVC). The accepted value for the density of PVC is 1.38 g/cm^3. The most likely reason for the difference between the accepted value and the experimental value is that:

   A. density depends on the mass but not the volume.
   B. density depends on the volume but not the mass.
   C. there was a measurement error that was consistent across samples.
   D. there was a measurement error that was inconsistent across samples.

LEVEL 4: INFERRING FROM DATA

4. Based on the data in the table, a 35 g sample of which substance would have the greatest volume?

   F. Sample 2
   G. Sample 3
   H. Sample 4
   J. Sample 6

168

Passage II

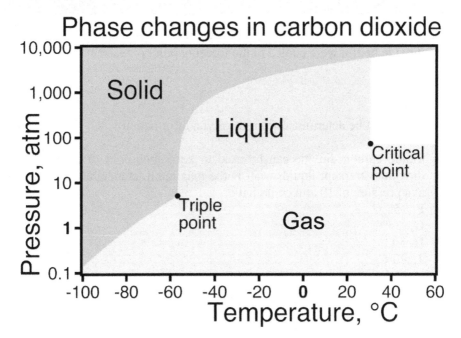

5. Suppose you had a sample of liquid carbon dioxide at -20°C at 100 atm. How could you cause the sample to freeze into a solid?

   A. Increase the temperature approximately 10°C
   B. Increase the temperature approximately 25°C
   C. Decrease the temperature approximately 10°C
   D. Decrease the temperature approximately 25°C

6. At a pressure of 100 atm, what phase would a 1,500 g sample of carbon dioxide be?

   F. Solid
   G. Liquid
   H. Gas
   J. Cannot be determined from the given information

LEVEL 5: INFERRING FROM DATA

7. At a pressure of 1 atm, what phase would a 10 mg sample of carbon dioxide be if it were cooled to the freezing point of water?

A. Solid
B. Liquid
C. Gas
D. Cannot be determined from the given information

8. Liquid carbon dioxide can be used to keep food cold. If the carbon dioxide were kept liquid, what is the maximum temperature a freezer at a pressure of 10 atm could have?

F. -55°C
G. -35°C
H. 5°C
J. 30°C

Answers

1. C	5. D
2. H	6. J
3. C	7. C
4. H	8. G

Full Solutions

2.

You are looking for a density between 0.917 g/cm³ and 0.940 g/cm³. Samples 4 and 5 both fall within that range. The answer is choice **H**.

3.

According to the text, mass and volume were measured before calculating density, so you can infer that both mass and volume are used to calculate density. On the table, Samples 1, 2, and 3 (top three rows of data) all have a density of 1.20 g/cm³, so any measurement error was likely consistent across samples and affected them all the same way. In other words, the measurement error made each sample 1.20 g/cm³ instead of 1.38 g/cm³. The answer is choice **C**.

4.

Density is the ratio of mass to volume, which you can calculate to confirm (you only need to calculate it for one sample to confirm). The sample with the greatest density will have the greatest ratio of mass to volume, so the sample with the lowest density will have the greatest volume for a given mass. Samples 4 and 5 have the lowest density, so a 35 g sample of Sample 4 will have the greatest volume of all four choices. The answer is choice **H**.

5.

In the figure, -20°C is on the x-axis (horizontal axis) near the middle. 100 atm is on the y-axis (vertical axis) near the middle. Trace the -20 line up to where it would meet the 100 line. Scan the answer choices to look at the suggestions, which are all about changing temperature. To get the liquid to freeze into a solid, you need to go left on the graph about 25°, which means decrease the temperature approximately 25°C. Thus, the answer is choice **D**.

6.

In the figure, 100 atm is on the y-axis (vertical axis), in the middle. If you follow that line across, you see that carbon dioxide can be either a solid or liquid, depending on the temperature. The temperature isn't given, so the answer is Cannot be determined from the given information, choice **J**.

7.

This question is similar to the previous question, but provides additional information. We have both the pressure and temperature, as long as we recognize that the freezing point of water is 0°C. Follow 0°C up from the x-axis (horizontal axis) and 1 atm to the right from the y-axis (vertical axis) to see that the sample of carbon dioxide would be a gas. The answer is choice **C**.

8.

Find 10 atm on the y-axis (vertical axis). It's just below the middle. Follow the 10 atm line across to the right to where the "liquid" area meets the "gas" area. This is around -35°C. If the temperature were greater than -35°C, carbon dioxide would be a gas. Thus, the temperature can be, at most, -35°C, which is choice **G**.

LESSON 22
SCIENCE CONTENT: CHEMISTRY

Chemistry consists of a blend of many topics. Chemistry topics range from atomic structure to pH to density, each of which appears quite frequently on the ACT. Understanding these basic concepts can help you navigate the science passages better.

How to Recognize

- The passage involves a chemistry concept or experiment, but the answer to a question is not in the text or figures.

How to Attack

- Get as much information as you can from the text and figures.
- Quickly scan the passage for the answer to each question, but assume you will need background knowledge for 1-2 questions per passage.

What to Know

All matter is made up of **atoms**. An atom is the smallest unit of a substance that still has the properties of that substance. That is, one atom of gold is the smallest possible amount of gold that is still shiny, yellowish, and valuable. Atoms are made up of **protons**, **neutrons**, and **electrons**. Protons and neutrons are found in the middle of the atom in an area called the **nucleus** (yes, the same word used to describe the middle of a cell). Electrons are much, much smaller than protons or neutrons and are found in a cloud around the outside of the nucleus. A proton has a positive charge. The number of protons in an atom determines which **element**, or type of atom, it is (hydrogen, oxygen, etc.). A neutron has no charge. An electron has a negative charge.

In a neutral atom, the number of protons equals the number of electrons, so the positive and negative charges cancel each other out. If the atom gains or loses an electron, it becomes an **ion** with a negative or positive charge.

172

Two or more atoms can combine to form **molecules**. Each substance is described by a **chemical formula**, which is a series of letters and numbers that describe the ratios among the different elements in the molecules of a substance. **Subscripts** are used to show how many of each element there are, whereas **coefficients** show how many whole molecules there are. Common examples are O_2, which shows two atoms of oxygen, and $6CO_2$, which shows 6 carbon dioxide molecules, each of which is made up of one carbon atom and two oxygen atoms. Most **organic** molecules (molecules that make up life), contain some combination of carbon (C), oxygen (O), hydrogen (H), and/or a few other elements such as chlorine (Cl), sulfur (S), and/or phosphorus (P).

A **solution** is a uniform mixture. The **solute**, such as Kool-Aid mix, is mixed into a **solvent**, such as water.

All substances have a **density**, which describes how tightly-packed the particles of a substance are. Any substance will float on denser substances and sink in less dense substances, as long as at least one of those substances is liquid or gas (you can't really float or sink on a solid). For example, salad dressing separates into oil at the top and vinegar on the bottom, because vinegar is more dense than oil.

pH is a measure of how acidic a substance is. Acidity is a measure of the concentration of hydrogen ions in a substance. pH is usually measured on a scale from 1-14. A pH of 7 is neutral. Anything less than 7 is considered **acidic** and anything more than 7 is considered **basic**. As pH decreases, acidity increases, and as pH increases, **alkalinity** (how basic a substance is) increases. Each change of 1 in a substance's pH is a tenfold change in acidity, so a substance with a pH of 3 is ten times more acidic than a substance with a pH of 4.

The freezing point of water is $0°C$, so water is solid (ice) at any temperature below $0°C$. Between $0°C$ and $100°C$, water is liquid. At exactly $0°C$, water can be both solid and liquid, but the ACT is unlikely to ask about the state of matter during a phase change. Between $0°C$ and $100°C$, water is liquid. $100°C$ is the boiling point of water, so water is gas at any temperature above $100°C$. This only holds true for pure H_2O. Mixing a solute into the water will change its melting and boiling point.

173

Try to answer the following question using the information in this lesson. These questions are always considered more difficult than they actually are because the ACT assumes you have not freshened up your chemistry knowledge since sophomore year. **Do not** check the solution until you have attempted this question yourself.

LEVEL 2: CHEMISTRY

1. Which of these subatomic particles has a positive charge?
   A. Electron
   B. Neutron
   C. Proton
   D. Orbital

Solution: Atoms are made up of three subatomic (smaller than an atom) particles. A proton (choice C), has a positive charge. A neutron (choice B) has no charge or a neutral charge, and an electron (choice A) has a negative charge. An orbital (choice D) is a region where electrons are likely to be found, outside of the atom's nucleus. The answer is choice **C**.

Try to answer the following questions using the information in this lesson. The answers to these questions, followed by full solutions, are at the end of this lesson. **Do not** look at the answers until you have attempted these questions yourself. Please remember to mark off any problems you get wrong. Questions 5-8 refer to the given passage; the rest of the questions stand alone.

LEVEL 2: CHEMISTRY

2. How many hydrogen atoms are in each water (H_2O) molecule?
   F. 0
   G. 1
   H. 2
   J. 3

LEVEL 3: CHEMISTRY

3. A dilute solution of hydrochloric acid is acidic. Which of the following could be its pH?

   A. 5.5
   B. 7.0
   C. 8.5
   D. 11.0

4. Helium has two protons it its nucleus. Which of the following molecules could be helium?

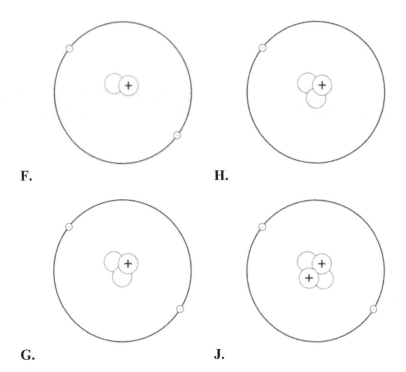

F.   **H.**

G.   **J.**

175

Passage 1

Students perform the following acid-base neutralization reaction.

$$2\ HCl + Mg(OH)_2 \rightarrow 2\ H_2O + MgCl_2$$

As shown in the chemical equation above, a strong acid (HCl) reacts with a strong base (Mg(OH)$_2$) to form water (H$_2$O) and magnesium chloride (MgCl$_2$).

5. At the end of the reaction, MgCl$_2$ was dissolved in the H$_2$O. Which substance acted as a solute?

A. Acid
B. Base
C. MgCl$_2$
D. H$_2$O

LEVEL 4: CHEMISTRY

6. If all the HCl was consumed in the reaction and 4 moles of MgCl$_2$ were produced, how many moles of HCl were initially present?

F. 1 mole
G. 2 moles
H. 4 moles
J. 8 moles

7. Which of the following substances likely has the lowest pH in solution?

A. Strong acid
B. Weak acid
C. Strong base
D. Weak base

LEVEL 5: CHEMISTRY

8. A scientist had a solution of $Mg(OH)_2$ that had a pH of 11.0. In order to change the pH of the solution to 9.0, the scientists should

F. Add acid until the acidity increases by a factor of 2.
G. Add acid until the acidity increases by a factor of 100.
H. Add base until the acidity decreases by a factor of 2.
J. Add base until the acidity decreases by a factor of 100.

Answers

1. C   5. C
2. H   6. J
3. A   7. A
4. J   8. G

Full Solutions

2.
In a chemical formula like H_2O, the subscript shows how many atoms of a certain element are in each molecule. Each molecule of H_2O has two hydrogen (H) atoms and one oxygen (O) atom, so the answer is choice **H**.

3.
An acid has a pH below 7. The only answer choice below 7 is 5.5. This is choice **A**. 7.0 Choice B is neutral and the other choices are basic.

4.
Protons are positively charged and would be represented by a "+" in the nucleus. The only answer choice that has two protons in the nucleus is choice **J**.

5.
The substance being dissolved is the solute and the substance its being dissolved in is the solvent. In this example, $MgCl_2$ is being dissolved in H_2O, so $MgCl_2$ is the solute. The answer is choice **C**.

6.

In a chemical equation, the coefficients show the ratio of moles used or produced in an equation. In the given equation, HCl has a coefficient of 2 and $MgCl_2$ has no coefficient, which means a 1 is implied. For every 2 moles of HCl that are used, 1 mole of $MgCl_2$ is produced. If 4 moles of $MgCl_2$ are produced, 8 moles of HCl must have been used. Therefore, the answer is choice **J**.

7.

Acids and bases are nearly always in solution, so that part of the question is unnecessary information. A low pH would be an acid. A strong acid would have a lower pH than a weak acid. The lowest pH would be a strong acid, which is choice **A**.

8.

An acid has a lower pH than a base. To lower a solution from a pH of 11.0 to a pH of 9.0, the acidity has to increase by a factor of 100 because each number on the pH scale is equivalent to a tenfold increase or decrease in acidity. Thus, acid needs to be added to increase the acidity by a factor of 100, and the answer is choice **G**.

LESSON 23
READING: CONVERTING TEXT TO DATA

Text-to-data questions will not show up on every single test, but they do tend to take students by surprise. Students looking to score a 32 or higher should be able to recognize these questions and conquer them, even though they might be different from any of the other questions. These questions require you to interpret information in the text and choose a graph or figure that represents the information accurately. The questions are usually not too difficult but can be confusing because they don't look like other questions.

How to Recognize

- Buzz words: which of the following figures, which of the following pie charts, which of the following graphs
- The answer choices will have a figure or graph.

How to Attack

- Identify any key words in the question.
- Find and underline the right line in the text.
- Jot down numbers if necessary.
- Cross out answer choices that are definitely wrong.

Don't Get Tricked

- Consider general trends (increase, decrease) but don't forget specific numbers as well.
- Double-check the key and axis labels.
- Jot down numbers so you don't mix them up.

Try to answer the following question using this strategy. **Do not** check the solution until you have attempted this question yourself.

LEVEL 2: CONVERTING TEXT TO DATA

Passage I

Students performed an experiment to investigate the properties of water. A 100 mg sample of ice was heated in a beaker. The students observed that the temperature remained the same until the ice had completely melted, at which point the temperature increased steadily throughout the rest of the experiment.

1. Which of the following diagrams is consistent with the description of the start of the experiment?

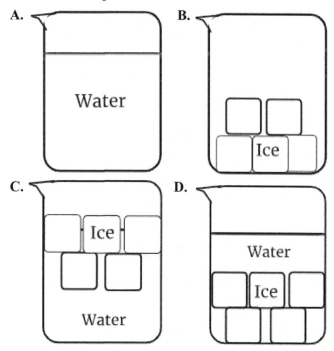

Solution: The text describing the start of the experiment states "A 100 mg sample of ice was heated in a beaker." Since only ice was mentioned, the only diagram that is consistent with the description is choice **B**.

Try to answer the following questions using the strategies in this lesson. Questions 2-4 refer to Passage I above. Questions 5-8 refer to Passage II, which can be found after Question 4. The answers to these questions, followed by full solutions, are at the end of this lesson. **Do not** look at the answers until you have attempted these questions yourself. Please remember to mark off any problems you get wrong.

LEVEL 2: CONVERTING TEXT TO DATA

2. Which of the following line graphs is most consistent with the description of temperature in relation to time *after* the ice had completely melted?

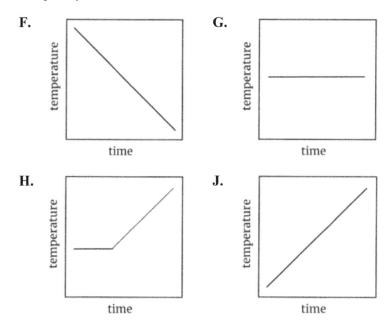

181

LEVEL 3: CONVERTING TEXT TO DATA

3. Which of the following pie charts is most consistent with the description of the water at the start of the experiment?

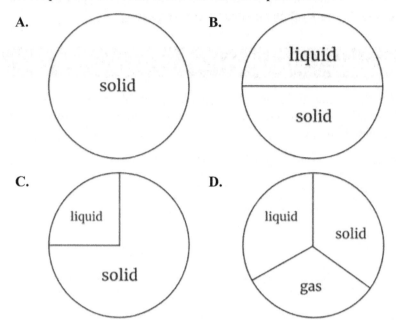

A. solid

B. liquid / solid

C. liquid / solid

D. liquid / solid / gas

4. Which of the following line graphs is most consistent with the description of temperature in relation to time throughout the entire experiment?

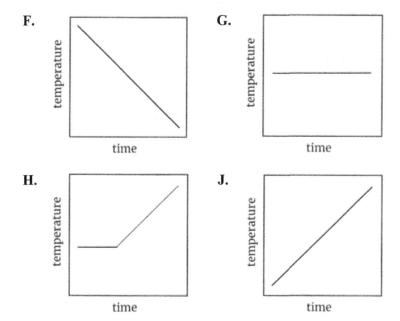

Passage II

A teacher performed a demonstration for a biology class using serial dilutions of a nutrient broth containing bacteria. The following steps were performed:

1. A test tube with nutrient broth was inoculated with one species of bacteria and allowed to grow in an incubator overnight.
2. A 1 mL sample of the bacteria broth was spread on an agar plate.
3. A 1 mL sample of the bacteria broth was added to a test tube with 9 mL sterile nutrient broth.
4. Steps 2-3 were repeated two additional times, to create two additional dilutions.
5. A 1 mL sample of the final dilution was spread on an agar plate.
6. Agar plates were incubated at 37°C overnight.
7. The number of colonies on each plate was recorded.

183

5. Which of the following figures is most consistent with the test tube described in Step 3?

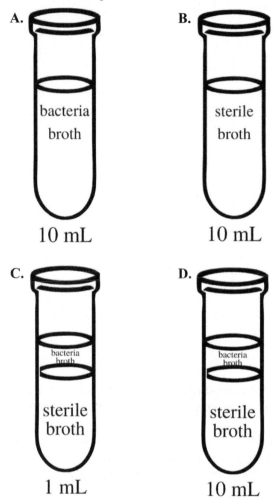

A.

bacteria
broth

10 mL

B.

sterile
broth

10 mL

C.

bacteria
broth

sterile
broth

1 mL

D.

bacteria
broth

sterile
broth

10 mL

184

LEVEL 4: CONVERTING TEXT TO DATA

6. Which of the following figures is most consistent with the description of the agar plates and dilutions used in the experiment?

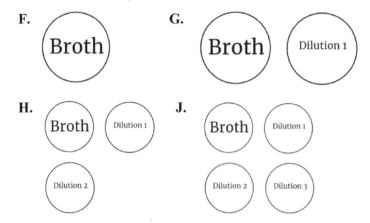

7. Which of the following figures is most consistent with the description of the serial dilutions in the experiment?

A.

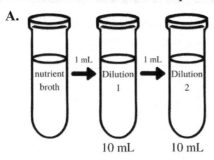

B.

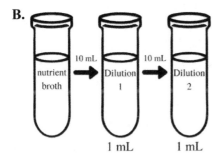

C.

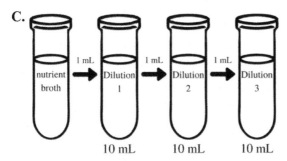

D.

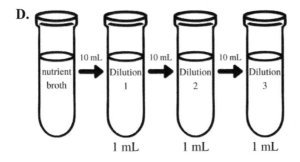

LEVEL 5: CONVERTING TEXT TO DATA

8. Which of the following tables is most consistent with the serial dilutions described in the experiment?

F.

Dilution	Bacterial colonies
Broth	10
Dilution 1	14
Dilution 2	18
Dilution 3	20

G.

Dilution	Bacterial colonies
Broth	18
Dilution 1	14
Dilution 2	10
Dilution 3	6

H.

Dilution	Bacterial colonies
Broth	10
Dilution 1	97
Dilution 2	800 (estimated)
Dilution 3	Too many to count

J.

Dilution	Bacterial colonies
Broth	Too many to count
Dilution 1	800 (estimated)
Dilution 2	99
Dilution 3	10

187

Answers

1. B	5. D
2. J	6. J
3. A	7. C
4. H	8. H

Full Solutions

2.

Scan the text for the word "melt". The text states "until the ice had completely melted, at which point the temperature increased steadily throughout the rest of the experiment." Steady increase looks like a diagonal line going up from left to right, which matches choice **J**.

3.

The text describing the start of the experiment states "A 100 mg sample of ice was heated in a beaker." Since only ice was mentioned, 100% of the water was in the solid state. The answer is choice **A**.

4.

The key portion of the text here is "the temperature remained the same until the ice had completely melted, at which point the temperature increased steadily throughout the rest of the experiment." Temperature staying the same would appear as a horizontal line on the graph. A steady increase looks like a diagonal line going up from left to right. The only graph that has a horizontal line followed by a steady increase is choice **H**.

5.

Step 3 says "A 1 mL sample of the broth was added to a test tube with 9 mL sterile nutrient broth." In other words, a small amount of bacteria broth was added to a larger amount of sterile broth to total 10 mL. The correct answer is choice **D**.

6.

Scan the description of the experiment for the word "plate". A sample was spread on a plate in Step 2. Step 2 was then repeated two more times for a total of three plates. Then, the final dilution is spread on a plate in Step 5. This uses four total plates (original broth plus three dilutions). The figure with four plates is choice **J**.

7.

In Step 3, 1 mL of the original broth was put in another test tube, which is two total test tubes. This was repeated two times, to add another two test tubes. A total of four test tubes (three dilutions) were used. Choices C and D have four test tubes. The amount of bacteria broth that was transferred to each dilution was 1 mL, so choose the diagram with 1 mL over the arrows. The answer is choice **C**.

8.

Each dilution uses 1 mL bacteria broth in 9 mL sterile broth, so is a roughly 10-fold dilution. The original sample would have ten times as many bacteria as the first dilution. The only table that has this relationship is choice **H**, because the numbers in the right column (number of colonies, which represents the number of bacteria present) decrease 10-fold each row.

LESSON 24
DATA ANALYSIS: CONVERTING DATA

A conversion question asks students to convert data from one form to another. For example, a question might ask to convert from a table to a graph, or from a line graph to a bar graph. These questions only show up about once every other test, but tend to be among the most confusing questions because there are multiple data points to keep straight.

How to Recognize

- Buzz words: is best represented by
- There are graphs in the answer choices.

How to Attack

- Circle the graph name if it's mentioned in the question.
- Figure out which data or trends will be needed to answer the question.
- Jot down values - trust me.
- Use process of elimination to eliminate the answer choices that are definitely wrong.

Don't Get Tricked

- Sometimes, you will be including data from multiple graphs, which may or may not have the same axis scales.

Try to answer the following question using this strategy. **Do not** check the solution until you have attempted this question yourself.

190

LEVEL 1: CONVERTING DATA

Passage I

Students investigated *osmosis* (diffusion of water across a semipermeable membrane) by putting cubes of raw potato into NaCl solutions of different concentrations. One potato cube was submerged in each solution for one hour. The mass of each potato cube was recorded before and after the experiment. The results are shown in the table.

Solution (mol NaCl/L H_2O)	Initial mass (grams)	Final mass (grams)	Change in mass (grams)
0	40.5	39.2	-1.3
0.2	43.2	40.0	-3.2
0.4	39.7	38.9	-0.8
0.6	44.9	45.4	0.5
0.8	40.1	43.8	3.7
1.0	42.2	45.6	3.4

1. According to the table, which of the following graphs best shows the initial and final mass of the potato cube submerged in solution that was 0.2 mol NaCl/L H_2O?

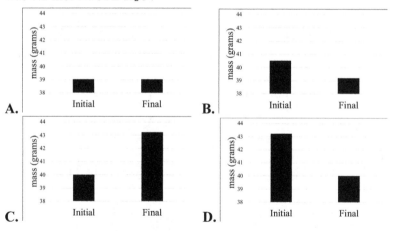

191

Solution: The question is looking for the initial and final mass of the potato in the 0.2 solution. The 0.2 solution is the second row of data in the table. Be very careful to avoid mixing up data points. The initial mass (second column from the left) is 43.2 g and the final mass (second column from the right) is 40.0 g. Eliminate choices A and C because the initial mass is lower or equal to the final mass in those graphs. Choice D is the only one that has an initial mass over 43 g. Therefore, the answer is choice **D**.

Try to answer the following questions using the strategies in this lesson. Questions 2-4 refer to Passage I above. Questions 5-8 refer to Passage II, which can be found after Question 4. The answers to these questions, followed by full solutions, are at the end of this lesson. **Do not** look at the answers until you have attempted these questions yourself. Please remember to mark off any problems you get wrong.

LEVEL 2: CONVERTING TEXT TO DATA

2. Which of the following figures is most consistent with the data in the table for the potato cube submerged in solution that was 0.8 mol NaCl/L H_2O?

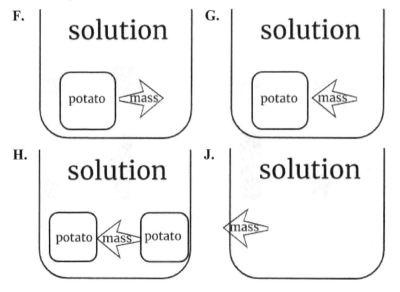

3. Which graph best represents the change in mass of the potato cubes for all concentrations of NaCl concentration?

A.

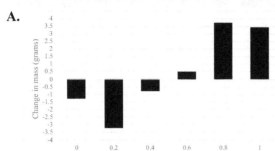

B.

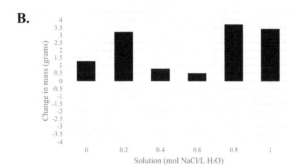

C.

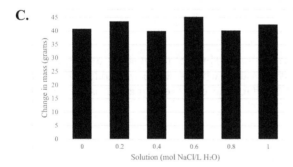

D.

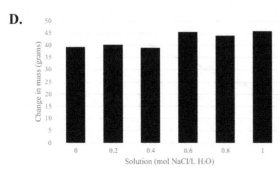

LEVEL 3: CONVERTING TEXT TO DATA

4. Which of the following figures is most consistent with the data in the table for the potato cube in the solution that was pure water?

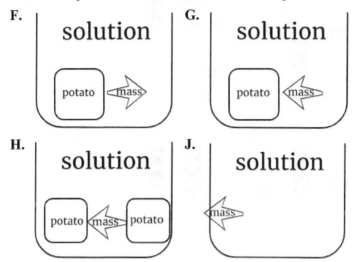

Passage II

Experiment 1

Students heated a sample of liquid H_2O in a beaker on a hot plate. The temperature was continuously measured while a solute was added. The solutes used were LiOH, KBr, and $NaNO_3$. The data were graphed as the solubility curves below.

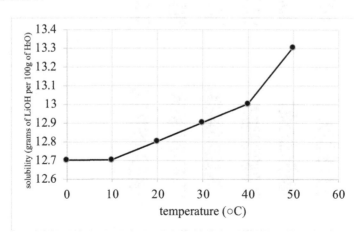

194

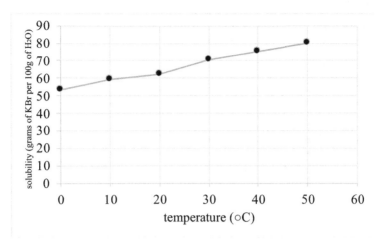

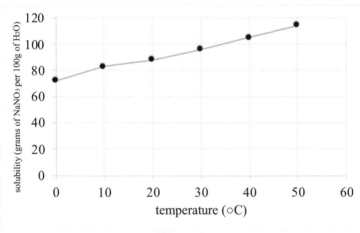

Figure 1

Experiment 2

Students repeated the experiment with NH₄Cl. Their data is shown in the table below.

Table 1	
temperature (°C)	solubility (grams of NH₄Cl per 100g of H₂O
0	21.5
20	38.6
40	46.9
60	55.1

5. Which graph best represents the solubility curve of NH_4Cl?

A.

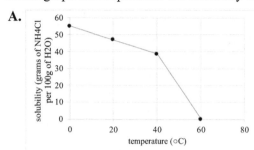

B.

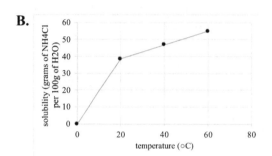

C.

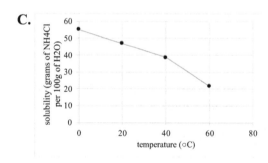

D.

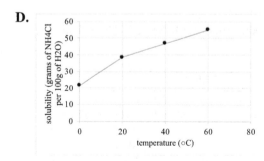

6. According to Figure 1, which of the following tables best shows, for LiOH, KBr, and NaNO$_3$, respectively, the solubility at 50°C?

F.

Solute	Solubility at 50°C (grams of solute per 100 g H$_2$O)
LiOH	114.9
KBr	80.1
NaNO$_3$	13.3

G.

Solute	Solubility at 50°C (grams of solute per 100 g H$_2$O)
LiOH	13.3
KBr	80.1
NaNO$_3$	114.9

H.

Solute	Solubility at 50°C (grams of solute per 100 g H$_2$O)
LiOH	12.7
KBr	53.5
NaNO$_3$	68.8

J.

Solute	Solubility at 50°C (grams of solute per 100 g H$_2$O)
LiOH	68.8
KBr	53.5
NaNO$_3$	12.7

7. According to Figure 1, which of the following graphs best shows, for LiOH, KBr, and NaNO₃, respectively, the solubility at 20°C?

A.

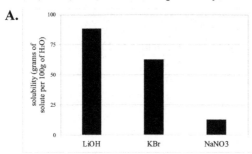

B.

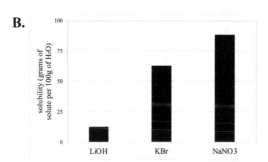

C.

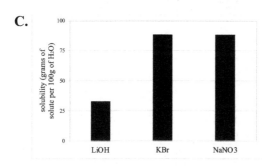

D.

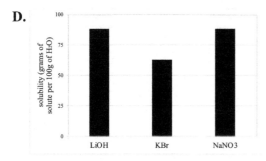

LEVEL 4: CONVERTING TEXT TO DATA

8. Which of the following pie charts best represents the percent of $NaNO_3$ and H_2O in the solution in the beaker at 30°C, assuming there was no precipitate present?

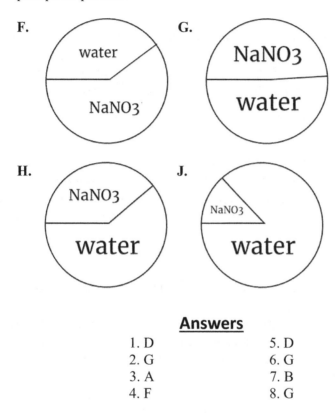

F.

G.

H.

J.

Answers

1. D	5. D
2. G	6. G
3. A	7. B
4. F	8. G

Full Solutions

2.

According to the table, when the solution was 0.8 mol NaCl/L H_2O (second row from the bottom), the initial mass of the potato was 40.1 g, the final mass was 43.8 g, and the change was 3.7 g. This tells us the potato *gained* mass. Since there is only one potato cube per solution, the potato must be gaining mass from the solution. The figure that best represents this is choice **G**.

3.

The change in mass of the potato cubes is shown in the rightmost column of the table. You can see there are both positive and negative values, so you can actually eliminate choices B, C, and D, which only have positive values. The answer is choice **A**.

4.

Pure water means the solution has no NaCl. According to the table, when the solution was 0 mol NaCl/L H_2O (top row of data), the initial mass of the potato is 40.5 g, the final mass is 39.2 g, and the change is -1.3 g. This tells us the potato *lost* mass. The figure that best represents this is choice **F**.

5.

On the table, solubility (right column) increases as temperature (left column) increases. The only graphs that show that relationship are choices B and D. Choice B has a solubility of 0 g at 0°C, which doesn't match the graph. So, we can eliminate choice B and the answer is choice **D**.

6.

Check the label along the y-axis on each graph to see which solute is shown. Also pay attention to the y-axes because the scales are different for each graph. For LiOH (top graph), at 50°C on the x-axis, the solubility is around 13.3 g. For KBr, the solubility is around 80 g and for NaNO3, the solubility is around 115 g. Choice **G** is the only table that has numbers close to these.

7.

Check the label along the y-axis on each graph to see which solute is shown. Also pay attention to the y-axes because the scales are different for each graph. For LiOH (top graph), at 20°C on the x-axis, the solubility is around 12.8 g. For KBr, the solubility is around 60 g and for NaNO3, the solubility is around 88 g. The answer choices have the solutes in the same order, so the bars should get taller from left to right. Choice B is the only graph that has the bars getting taller from left to right. Therefore, the answer is choice **B**.

8.

NaNO$_3$ is the bottom graph in Figure 1, according to the label along the
y-axis. At 30°C on the x-axis, NaNO$_3$ is about 98 g per 100g of H$_2$O.
Those numbers are very close, so there is about 50% NaNO$_3$ and 50%
H$_2$O in solution at that temperature. The pie chart that best represents
50/50 is choice G because the pie is split roughly in half. Therefore, the
answer is choice **G**.

LESSON 25
SCIENCE CONTENT: EARTH/SPACE SCIENCE

Earth and Space Science aren't usually studied in high school, so these topics can catch students off guard. Students often have personal experience with many of these concepts, so common sense can go a long way. This lesson will present some basic skills that will help students interpret many Earth and Space Science passages that might come up.

How to Recognize

- Buzz words: climate, erosion, weathering, soil, sediment

How to Attack

- Get as much information as you can from the text and figures.
- Quickly scan the passage for the answers to the question, but assume you will need background knowledge for 1-2 questions per passage.
- If in doubt, lean on common sense.

What to Know

The **water cycle** describes the way water moves through the atmosphere in a pattern. Water **evaporates** when it turns from liquid water to water vapor and enters the atmosphere. Evaporation is greater with higher temperatures. **Transpiration** is when liquid water turns into water vapor and is released from plants. Water vapor in the atmosphere accumulates and **condenses** into liquid water again, where it falls as **precipitation**. This water will usually roll downhill and accumulate in lakes and oceans, where it begins the cycle again.

The movement of water and other factors cause the breakdown of rock, called **weathering**. The movement of these broken down rock particles (**sediments**), usually downhill, is called **erosion**.

Global warming, or global **climate change**, refers to the long-term changes in the Earth's climate. **Climate** is long-term temperature and moisture patterns, compared to the shorter-term **weather**. Climate change is accelerated by human activity, including the release of **greenhouse gases** into the atmosphere. These gases, such as **carbon dioxide** (CO_2) and **methane** (CH_4), trap the sun's radiation in Earth's atmosphere, causing the planet's temperature to rise. Greenhouse gases do not create heat on their own; rather, they trap the sun's heat in Earth's atmosphere.

The sun is the center of our Solar System and is orbited by eight planets. The first four planets (Mercury, Venus, Earth, Mars) are called terrestrial planets because they are rocky, like Earth. The gas giants (Jupiter, Saturn, Uranus, Neptune) are farther from the sun, are made of gas, and are larger than terrestrial planets.

Try to answer the following question using the information in this lesson. These questions are always considered more difficult than they actually are because the ACT assumes you have not freshened up your Earth and Space Science knowledge since middle school. **Do not** check the solution until you have attempted this question yourself.

LEVEL 2: EARTH/SPACE SCIENCE

1. Which of the following processes most directly increases the amount of water in Earth's atmosphere?

   A. Condensation
   B. Precipitation
   C. Evaporation
   D. Runoff

Solution: Evaporation (choice C) is the change of phase from liquid to gas. In the Water Cycle, this means water in the form of liquid, such as in oceans and rivers, is converting into water vapor, in the atmosphere. Condensation (choice A) is the change from gas to liquid and precipitation (choice B) is when this liquid falls to Earth, both processes that move water away from the atmosphere. Runoff (choice D) is when water that has not been absorbed into the ground moves from higher elevation to lower elevation. The answer is evaporation, choice **C**.

Try to answer the following questions using the information in this lesson. The answers to these questions, followed by full solutions, are at the end of this lesson. **Do not** look at the answers until you have attempted these questions yourself. Please remember to mark off any problems you get wrong. All of these questions relate to background knowledge only; there are no figures, graphs, or text.

LEVEL 2: EARTH/SPACE SCIENCE

2. Which of the following planets is a gas giant?

    F. Mercury
    G. Venus
    H. Earth
    J. Jupiter

3. Which of the following processes only occurs in the presence of plants?

    A. Condensation
    B. Transpiration
    C. Evaporation
    D. Precipitation

LEVEL 3: EARTH/SPACE SCIENCE

4. Which of the following gases contributes to the Greenhouse Effect in Earth's atmosphere?

    F. Oxygen (O_2)
    G. Nitrogen (N_2)
    H. Argon (Ar)
    J. Methane (CH_4)

5. Which of the following planets is most similar to Earth?

    A. Mars
    B. Jupiter
    C. Saturn
    D. Neptune

LEVEL 4: EARTH/SPACE SCIENCE

6. Scientists have recently located another star system with several planets orbiting a medium-sized star. Which of the following planets would be most promising for scientists to look for signs of life?

F. Terrestrial planet with liquid water present
G. Terrestrial planet without liquid water present
H. Gas giant with liquid water present
J. Gas giant without liquid water present

7. How does methane contribute to Global Warming?

A. Methane reacts with the oxygen in the air to create a combustion reaction, which releases heat into Earth's atmosphere.
B. Methane has high molecular kinetic energy, which increases the temperature of the surrounding air.
C. Methane traps heat radiated from the Earth, causing the atmosphere's temperature to increase.
D. Methane reacts with carbon dioxide to release heat into Earth's atmosphere.

8. Which of the following is the most likely path for weathered sediment?

F. Sediment is carried up the side of a mountain in a stream, where it eventually reaches the mountain top and settles into the soil.
G. Sediment is carried down the side of a mountain in a stream, where it eventually reaches the ocean and settles to the bottom of the ocean floor.
H. Sediment is carried down the side of a mountain in a stream, where the stream continues up to the top of the next mountain and the sediment settles into the soil.
J. Sediment is carried up the side of a mountain in a stream, where it is layered on top of additional layers of sediment.

Answers

1. C	5. A
2. J	6. F
3. B	7. C
4. J	8. G

Full Solutions

2.

Jupiter, Saturn, Uranus, and Neptune are all gas giants because they are, quite literally, giant balls of gas. The other planets listed are terrestrial, which means they are rocky, like Earth. Thus, the answer is Jupiter, choice **J**.

3.

Transpiration (choice B) is when liquid water turns into water vapor and is released from plants. Evaporation (C) is the change of phase from liquid to gas. Condensation (A) is the change from gas to liquid and precipitation (D) is when this liquid falls to Earth. The answer is transpiration, choice **B**.

4.

Methane (choice J) is one of the strongest Greenhouse Gases, along with carbon dioxide (CO_2). Oxygen (choice F) and nitrogen (choice G) make up most of the air we breathe, but don't trap heat in Earth's atmosphere. Argon (choice H) is also present in the air and doesn't trap heat. The answer is methane, choice **J**.

5.

Mars (choice A) is the only planet listed that is a terrestrial (rocky) planet and similar in size to Earth. Jupiter, Saturn, and Neptune are all gas giants that are made of gas and are much, much bigger than Earth. The answer is Mars, choice **A**.

6.

Earth is a terrestrial (rocky) planet. Gas giants are much larger than Earth, so have gravity that is much too strong for living organisms to thrive. Living organisms also need liquid water to survive, so the most promising planet would be terrestrial with liquid water. Thus, the answer is choice **F**.

7.

Greenhouse gases heat Earth's atmosphere by trapping heat that is radiated from Earth. The most accurate answer is choice **C**. The other answer choices are factually incorrect.

8.

Sediment, or weathered pieces of rock, are often moved by water, wind and gravity downhill. Water almost always carries sediment downhill, so the most likely sediment path is choice **G**, which has the sediment traveling downhill only.

LESSON 26
INTEGRATED PRACTICE: TABLES AND GRAPHS

By now, you should have seen and practiced all of the question types you are likely to see in ACT Science.

On a real science section, about two out of the six passages are usually of the "tables and graphs" variety. That is, they don't have an experiment or a lot of text. They are mostly tables and graphs, and the questions are almost all answered using only the tables and graphs.

The following passage resembles a "tables and graphs" passage you might see on an ACT, with questions at all difficulty levels and getting progressively more difficult. The answers to these questions, followed by full solutions, are at the end of this lesson. **Do not** look at the answers until you have attempted these questions yourself. Please remember to mark off any problems you get wrong.

LEVEL 1: TABLES AND GRAPHS

Passage I

When a solid is heated, its molecules begin to move faster and faster. Given the right circumstances, the substance will eventually change from solid to liquid to gas. As heat is absorbed, temperature increases, until a phase change occurs. From the start to the finish of the phase change, temperature remains the same, while any absorbed heat contributes to the phase change. The amount of heat required to change a substance from solid to liquid, per gram of substance, is the *heat of fusion*. The amount of heat required to change a substance from liquid to gas, per gram of a substance, is the *heat of vaporization*. The heat of fusion and heat of vaporization for several substances are shown on Table 1.

Table 1		
Substance	Heat of Fusion (calories/gram)	Heat of Vaporization (calories/gram)
Water	80	540
Zinc	24	423
Gold	15	407

208

Students put a beaker of ice (solid H_2O) onto a heating plate and suspended a thermometer so its bulb was in the middle of the ice without touching the sides of the beaker. The beaker was heated for 15 minutes and temperature was recorded every minute. Figure 1 shows the recorded temperature of the H_2O during the experiment.

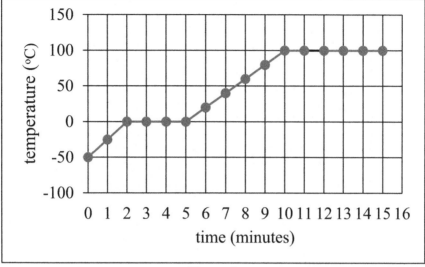

Figure 1

1. According to Table 1, what is the heat of vaporization for water (H_2O) in calories per gram?

   A. 15 calories/gram
   B. 80 calories/gram
   C. 407 calories/gram
   D. 540 calories/gram

LEVEL 2: TABLES AND GRAPHS

2. Which of the following diagrams is most consistent with the description of the beaker in the experiment while it was heated?

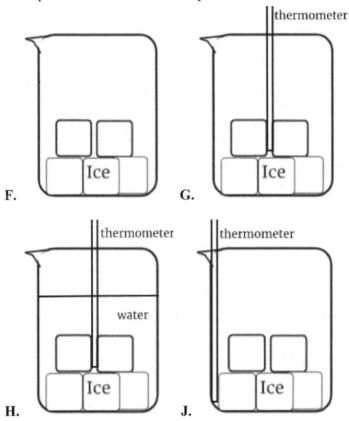

F.   G.   H.   J.

3. According to Figure 1, as water was heated from 5 to 15 minutes after the start of the experiment, the temperature of the water:

A. increased only.
B. decreased only.
C. increased, then decreased.
D. increased, then stayed the same.

LEVEL 3: TABLES AND GRAPHS

4. How much heat is required to turn a 10 g sample of zinc from solid to liquid?

   F. 24 calories
   G. 240 calories
   H. 423 calories
   J. 4230 calories

LEVEL 4: TABLES AND GRAPHS

5. According to the data in Figure 1, the water in the experiment was most likely changing phase:

   A. between 2 and 5 minutes after the start of the experiment.
   B. between 5 and 6 minutes after the start of the experiment.
   C. between 5 and 10 minutes after the start of the experiment.
   D. between 8 and 10 minutes after the start of the experiment.

6. Suppose water had a heat of fusion that was 10 times as great. How would the experiment most likely have been different?

   F. The ice would have taken a longer time to melt because it would have required more heat to change from solid to liquid.
   G. The ice would have taken a shorter time to melt because it would have required less heat to change from a solid to liquid.
   H. The water would have taken a longer time to boil because it would have required more heat to change from liquid to gas.
   J. The water would have taken a shorter time to boil because it would have required less heat to change from a liquid to a gas.

LEVEL 5: TABLES AND GRAPHS

7. The students used 20 grams of water, how much heat was added between 2 minutes and 5 minutes?

   A. 80 calories
   B. 160 calories
   C. 1,600 calories
   D. 10,800 calories

211

8. A liquid is considered a good *thermal insulator* if it does not easily change temperature or phase when heat is added. Which of the substances on Table 1 would most likely make the best thermal insulator?

F. Water; it requires more energy to change from liquid to gas than zinc or gold.
G. Water; it requires less energy to change from liquid to gas than zinc or gold.
H. Gold; it requires more energy to change from liquid to gas than water or zinc.
J. Gold; it requires less energy to change from liquid to gas than water or zinc.

Answers

1. D	5. A
2. G	6. F
3. D	7. C
4. G	8. F

Full Solutions

1.

In Table 1, heat of vaporization is the rightmost column. Water is in the top row of data, so the heat of vaporization for water is 540 calories/gram. Thus, the answer is choice **D**.

2.

The experiment describes a beaker with ice only, so eliminate choice B. The thermometer is suspended in the middle of the ice without touching the sides, so eliminate choices F and J. The only remaining diagram is choice **G**.

3.

In Figure 1, time is on the x-axis (horizontal axis) and temperature is on the y-axis (vertical axis). As time goes left to right from 5 to 15 minutes (the entire graph except for the left third), the line representing temperature increases then stays the same. The answer is choice **D**.

4.

According to the text, heat of fusion is the amount of heat required to change a substance from solid to liquid, *per gram of substance*. In Table 1, zinc is the middle row of data. The heat of fusion of zinc (middle column) is 24 calories/gram. To figure out the total number of calories, multiply 24 calories/gram by 10 grams. The answer is 240 calories, choice **G**.

5.

According to the text, temperature doesn't change during a phase change. The graph has temperature on the *y*-axis (vertical axis), so a phase change would occur when the line isn't changing vertically, or is a straight horizontal line. This occurs twice: from 2 to 5 minutes and from 10 to 15 minutes. The correct answer is choice **A**.

6.

According to the text, heat of fusion is the amount of heat required to turn a solid into a liquid. If water had a much bigger heat of fusion, it would have required much more heat to go from solid to liquid (melt). Since it would have required more heat, it would have taken longer to melt. The answer is choice **F**. You can eliminate H and J because heat of fusion has nothing to do with boiling.

7.

According to the text, temperature doesn't change during a phase change. The graph has temperature on the *y*-axis (vertical axis), so a phase change would occur when the line isn't changing vertically, or is a straight horizontal line. The phase change between 2 and 5 minutes is melting, because 0°C is the melting point of water (you should know that – also, the boiling point of water is 100°C). From 2 to 5 minutes, the sample of water goes through the entire phase change, which means it goes from entirely solid to entirely liquid. According to Table 1, the heat of fusion of water is 80 calories/gram, which means water requires 80 calories/gram to go from solid to liquid. There were 20 grams of water, so the total heat required for the phase change is 20 grams times 80 calories/gram, which is 1600 calories. Thus, the answer is choice **C**.

8.

We are looking for a material whose phase does not change to a gas easily, which means we are looking for something that requires a lot of energy to change it from a liquid to a gas. Heat of vaporization is the energy required to heat a substance from liquid to gas, so we need to find the highest heat of vaporization. The highest heat of vaporization in Table 1 is 540 calories/gram, in the right column, which corresponds to water. Water would make the best thermal insulator. The answer is choice **F**.

LESSON 27
INTEGRATED PRACTICE: EXPERIMENTS

By now, you should have seen and practiced all of the question types you are likely to see in ACT Science.

In a real science section, about half of the six passages are usually of the "experiments" variety. They have descriptions of one or more experiments, along with some tables and graphs. Most of the questions are answered using the tables and graphs, but some of them relate to the experiment's design too.

The following passage resembles an "experiments" passage you might see on an ACT, with questions at all difficulty levels and getting progressively more difficult. The answers to these questions, followed by full solutions, are at the end of this lesson. **Do not** look at the answers until you have attempted these questions yourself. Please remember to mark off any problems you get wrong.

LEVEL 1: EXPERIMENTS

Passage I

The zebrafish (*Danio rerio*) is often used to study genetics because its genome has been widely studied in the past. As a vertebrate, it shares many genes in common with humans and other animals, so investigation of zebrafish genes can yield useful information about human genetics.

Nuclease is an enzyme that breaks up DNA at a specific location. The process of repairing DNA often results in mutations, so nuclease is a tool that scientists can use to create mutations in specific genes. Scientists will often study genes by inactivating them, using nuclease, to observe the results in an organism without a specific functioning gene.

Experiment 1

Scientists wanted to investigate the effects of the *D. rerio* gene known as slc24a5 on zebrafish survival. When this gene is mutated, zebrafish develop a much lighter *pigmentation* (color). Mutations were introduced into the slc24a5 gene of 50 developing zebrafish embryos by injecting them with synthetic nuclease. These zebrafish embryos were allowed to develop into adult zebrafish and then they were observed in the laboratory.

50 additional zebrafish embryos were not injected with nuclease and allowed to develop into adult zebrafish, in an identical habitat with identical nutrition.

The survival of zebrafish during the course of the experiment was recorded in Figure 1.

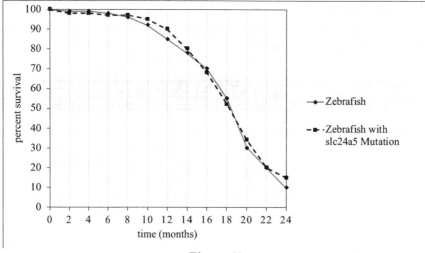

Figure 1

Experiment 2

Experiment 1 was repeated, except with a synthetic nuclease that targeted the ryr1a gene. The ryr1a gene is involved in binding calcium ions and is important for many functions in both zebrafish and humans. The results of Experiment 2 are shown in Figure 2.

216

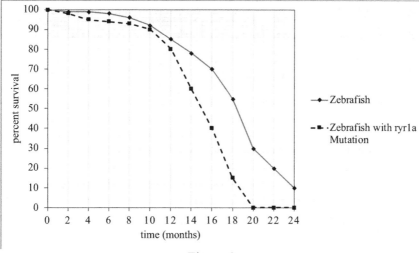

Figure 2

1. According to Figure 2, what was the percent survival of zebrafish with the ryr1a mutation after 12 months?

   A. 20%
   B. 30%
   C. 80%
   D. 90%

LEVEL 2: EXPERIMENTS

2. In Experiment 1, from month 0 to month 24, the population of zebrafish *without* the mutation:

   F. increased only.
   G. decreased only.
   H. increased, then decreased.
   J. decreased, then increased.

3. Suppose the zebrafish population with the ryr1a mutation had been measured at 15 months after the start of the experiment. The percent survival would most likely have been:

   A. less than 40%
   B. between 40% and 58%
   C. between 58% and 70%
   D. greater than 80%

217

LEVEL 3: EXPERIMENTS

4. Experiments 1 and 2 were carried out concurrently (at the same time). How long did the experiments last?

   F. 2 months
   G. 1 year
   H. 2 years
   J. Cannot be determined from the given information

5. Which of the following factors were kept the same between both experimental groups in Experiment 1?

   A. How much synthetic nuclease was injected
   B. Percent survival
   C. Zebrafish habitat
   D. Presence of the mutation

LEVEL 4: EXPERIMENTS

6. The control group in Experiment 2 was the:

   F. zebrafish without the ryr1a mutation
   G. zebrafish with the ryr1a mutation
   H. zebrafish with the slc24a5 mutation
   J. zebrafish injected with synthetic nuclease

7. Based on Figures 1 and 2, which gene mutation most likely had a greater impact on zebrafish survival?

   A. slc24a5; Experiment 1 showed greater variation in percent survival between the wild type zebrafish and the zebrafish with the mutation.
   B. slc24a5; Experiment 2 showed greater variation in percent survival between the wild type zebrafish and the zebrafish with the mutation.
   C. ryr1a; Experiment 1 showed greater variation in percent survival between the wild type zebrafish and the zebrafish with the mutation.
   D. ryr1a; Experiment 2 showed greater variation in percent survival between the wild type zebrafish and the zebrafish with the mutation.

LEVEL 5: EXPERIMENTS

8. Based on the description of the experiment and the data in Figure 2, approximately how many zebrafish with the ryr1a mutation died in the first 18 months of the experiment?

   F. 10
   G. 15
   H. 30
   J. 40

Answers

1. C	5. C
2. G	6. F
3. B	7. D
4. H	8. J

Full Solutions

1.

Figure 2 shows percent survival on the y-axis (vertical axis) and time in months on the x-axis (horizontal axis). Zebrafish *with* the mutation are represented by the dashed line. Follow the 12 months line up to the dotted line, which is around 80%. The answer is choice **C**.

2.

The results of Experiment 1 are shown in Figure 1. The time 0-24 months refers to the whole experiment, according to the x-axis, so we are looking at the entire graph. The zebrafish population *without* the mutation is represented by the solid line, which decreases throughout the experiment. Thus, the answer is choice **G**.

3.

Figure 2 corresponds to the experiment with the ryr1a mutation, according to its key. The population with the ryr1a mutation is represented by the dashed line. The x-axis (horizontal axis) is time. Find 15 months along the x-axis, which is halfway between the 14 and 16 marks. Follow the light 15 month line upwards to where it meets the dashed line, around 50% survival. The best answer is 40%-58%, choice **B**.

219

4.

To answer this question, look at the x-axis (horizontal axis), which represents time, on either graph. The graphs covered month 0 to month 24, which is 2 years because there are 12 months in a year. The answer is choice **H**.

5.

We can eliminate a couple of answer choices just by looking at the graphs. Percent survival (choice B) is on the y-axis (vertical axis), which means it is probably the dependent variable, or measured variable, and not the same between groups. The key of either graphs shows that the two groups were the group with the mutation and the group without the mutation, so the presence of the mutation (choice D) was not kept the same. If we look at the description of the experiment in the text, we see that the habitat and nutrition were identical between groups, in the second paragraph of Experiment 1. Thus, the answer is choice **C**.

6.

The control group is the group that gets no treatment and is compared to the experimental group. In Experiment 2, the experimental group was the group of zebrafish that had the ryr1a mutation (choice G), so the control group would have been the group that did not have the ryr1a mutation. The answer is choice **F**.

7.

In Figure 1, the zebrafish with the slc24a5 mutation (dashed line) had a very similar line to the zebrafish without the mutation (solid line), so we can assume the mutation did not have a big effect on survival. In Figure 2, however, there is a bigger difference between the zebrafish line and the zebrafish with ryr1a mutation line, with the mutated zebrafish surviving *less* than the wild type zebrafish. Thus, we can assume that the ryr1a mutation had a great effect on survival and the answer is choice **D**.

8.

According to Figure 2, at 18 months on the x-axis (horizontal axis), which represents time, the zebrafish with ryr1a mutation survival is around 15% on the y-axis (vertical axis), which shows percent survival. According to the description of Experiment 1, 50 fish with the mutation were studied, and Experiment 2 was a repeat of Experiment 1 with the ryr1a mutation. Since the scientists started with 50 fish, and only 15% survived after 18 months, there were roughly 0.15 x 50=7.5 fish surviving at that point. Since 50 − 7.5 = 42.5, approximately 42.5 fish had died in the first 18 months. The closest answer is choice **J**.

LESSON 28
INTEGRATED PRACTICE: CONFLICTING VIEWPOINTS

By now, you should have seen and practiced all of the question types you are likely to see in ACT Science.

Each ACT Science section has one "conflicting viewpoints" passage. These passages include several arguments by students or scientists about a single topic. Each argument tends to be formatted identically, so if one argument has a statement about Tyrannosaurus Rex pedal anatomy in the first sentence, the other arguments will also most likely talk about Tyrannosaurus Rex pedal anatomy in their first sentences as well. Nearly all of the questions on these passages will have answers found explicitly in the text.

The following passage resembles a "conflicting viewpoints" passage you might see on an ACT, with questions at all difficulty levels and getting progressively more difficult. The answers to these questions, followed by full solutions, are at the end of this lesson. **Do not** look at the answers until you have attempted these questions yourself. Please remember to mark off any problems you get wrong.

LEVEL 1: CONFLICTING VIEWPOINTS

Passage I

Many people die of *cardiovascular disease* every year. Cardiovascular disease is a disease that involves inflammation in the arteries, which eventually leads to narrowing and blockages of the arterial passages. These blockages can cause heart attacks and strokes. Cardiovascular disease is correlated with high levels of cholesterol in the blood.

Students discuss the role dietary cholesterol plays in cardiovascular disease.

Student 1

Dietary cholesterol is the primary source of high blood cholesterol levels. High blood cholesterol levels, especially high levels of high-density lipoprotein, contribute to cardiovascular disease and increase the risk of heart attacks and strokes. Reducing the intake of dietary cholesterol will lower blood cholesterol levels, which will reduce the risk of cardiovascular disease.

The most important thing people can do to prevent cardiovascular disease is restrict their dietary cholesterol to 300 mg/day. Other lifestyle changes, such as exercise, do not have as much of an impact on cardiovascular disease.

Student 2

Dietary cholesterol contributes to blood cholesterol levels, but is not the most significant factor. Blood cholesterol levels are also affected by overall diet, such as intake of saturated fats, and exercise. High blood cholesterol levels, including both high-density lipoprotein and low-density lipoprotein, contribute to cardiovascular disease and increase the risk of heart attacks and strokes. Reducing the intake of dietary cholesterol will lower blood cholesterol levels, which will reduce the risk of cardiovascular disease.

To prevent cardiovascular disease, people should restrict their dietary cholesterol to 300 mg/day and saturated fat to 22 g/day, maintain a healthy BMI, and exercise regularly.

Student 3

Dietary cholesterol has no impact on blood cholesterol levels. However, most foods high in cholesterol are also high in saturated fats, which increase the risk of cardiovascular disease. Although unrelated to diet, high blood cholesterol levels, especially high levels of high-density lipoprotein, contribute to cardiovascular disease and increase the risk of heart attacks and strokes

To prevent cardiovascular disease, people should eat a diet low in saturated fat, but do not need to restrict dietary cholesterol.

1. According to Student 3, which type of lipoprotein most contributes to cardiovascular disease?

   A. High-density lipoprotein only
   B. Low-density lipoprotein only
   C. Both high-density lipoprotein and low-density lipoprotein
   D. Neither high-density lipoprotein nor low-density lipoprotein

2. Which student, if any, argued that dietary cholesterol is the main source of blood cholesterol?

   F. Student 1
   G. Student 2
   H. Student 3
   J. None of the students

LEVEL 2: CONFLICTING VIEWPOINTS

3. Which student would agree that a diet low in dietary cholesterol reduces the risk of cardiovascular disease?

   A. Student 1 only
   B. Student 2 only
   C. Students 1 and 2 only
   D. Students 1, 2, and 3

4. According to Student 2, what are the maximum amounts of dietary cholesterol and saturated fat a person should consume in a day in order to limit the risk of cardiovascular disease?

	dietary cholesterol	saturated fat
F.	300 mg	300 mg
G.	300 mg	22 g
H.	22 g	300 mg
J.	22 g	22 g

224

LEVEL 3: CONFLICTING VIEWPOINTS

5. Which students would most likely agree with the statement "high blood cholesterol contributes directly to cardiovascular disease"?

   A. Student 1 only
   B. Students 1 and 2 only
   C. Student 2 only
   D. Students 1, 2, and 3

6. Which lifestyle intervention was not suggested by any of the students as a way to reduce the risk of cardiovascular disease?

   F. Restrict dietary cholesterol
   G. Restrict sugar intake
   H. Restrict saturated fat
   J. Exercise regularly

LEVEL 4: CONFLICTING VIEWPOINTS

7. A person diagnosed with cardiovascular disease would most likely have:

   A. blockages in the liver.
   B. brain inflammation.
   C. narrow or blocked blood vessels.
   D. unusually wide blood vessels.

8. Suppose the latest recommendation from the medical community was to consume no more than 9% of daily calories from saturated fat. For a person who consumes 1600 calories per day, how many of those calories should be saturated fat?

   F. 9 calories per day
   G. 144 calories per day
   H. 178 calories per day
   J. 14,400 calories per day

225

Answers

1. A	5. D
2. F	6. G
3. C	7. C
4. G	8. G

Full Solutions

1.

Scan Student 3's argument for the word "lipoprotein." Student 3 states in the last sentence of the first paragraph, "high cholesterol levels, especially high levels of high-density lipoprotein, contribute to cardiovascular disease." Thus, the answer is choice **A**.

2.

Student 1 states, "Dietary cholesterol is the primary source of high blood cholesterol levels" in the first sentence. The first sentence of each of the other arguments explicitly state that dietary cholesterol is *not* the main source of high blood cholesterol levels. The answer is choice **F**.

3.

In the last sentence of each of their arguments, Students 1 and 2 both suggest limiting dietary cholesterol to prevent cardiovascular disease. Student 3 suggests limiting saturated fat, but not dietary cholesterol. The answer is choice **C**.

4.

This question is easy to answer, but also easy to mix up. Jot down the numbers if you think you might switch them. Student 2 states, "people should restrict their dietary cholesterol to 300 mg/day and saturated fat to 22 g/day," so you need the answer that has 300 mg for cholesterol and 22 g for saturated fat. The answer is choice **G**.

5.

Student 1's second sentence states, "High blood cholesterol levels, especially high levels of high-density lipoprotein, contribute to cardiovascular disease." This sentence shows up in a similar location in Student 2's and Student 3's arguments, with only changes in the type of lipoprotein mentioned. Thus, all three students agree and the answer is choice **D**.

6.

The recommendations are found in the last sentence of each argument. Student 1 suggests restricting dietary cholesterol (choice F). Student 2 suggests restricting cholesterol and saturated fat (choice H), maintaining a healthy BMI, and exercising regularly (choice J). "Restrict sugar intake" is the only one not mentioned, so the answer is choice **G**.

7.

The first paragraph of the text states, "Cardiovascular disease is a disease that involves inflammation in the arteries, which eventually leads to narrowing and blockages of the arterial passages." Arteries are blood vessels, so the answer is choice **C**.

8.

9% of 1600 is 0.09 x 1600 = 144. The answer is choice **G**. You won't have a calculator, so the fastest way to get the answer is to estimate. 10% of 1600 is 160, so you want an answer that is just under 160.

ACTIONS TO COMPLETE AFTER YOU HAVE READ THIS BOOK

1. Take another practice ACT

You should see a substantial improvement in your score.

2. Continue to practice ACT science problems for 10 to 20 minutes each day

Review science questions and passages you've already completed to keep the concepts and strategies fresh in your mind. Practice new science passages from official practice tests and past exams, completing entire timed Science sections for the most authentic practice.

3. 'Like' my Facebook page

This page is updated regularly with ACT prep advice, tips, tricks, strategies, and practice problems. Visit the following webpage and click the 'like' button.

www.facebook.com/ACTPrepGet800

4. Review this book

If this book helped you, please post your positive feedback on the site you purchased it from; e.g. Amazon, Barnes and Noble, etc.

5. Register for updates

If you have not done so yet, visit the following webpage and enter your email address to receive additional content when it becomes available.

www.satprepget800.com/28LesAdv

About the Author

Dr. Satty is the owner of STEMsmart Consulting, an innovative consulting company that allows organizations to reach every student and provide remarkable STEM education. She holds an Ed.D in STEM Education from the University of Pittsburgh, and an Sc. M and Sc.B in Biology from Brown University. She is a certified teacher in three states and has been teaching in the classroom and tutoring test prep for more than a decade.

As a STEM education consultant, Dr. Satty has advised STEM programs across the US and contributed to several books on test prep, including writing the science answer explanations in The Unofficial ACT Solutions Manual. She has also developed NGSS- and CCSS-aligned STEM curricula and created tutor and teacher professional development programs on content, student assessment, and curriculum design.

Dr. Satty can be reached at

robin@stemsmartconsulting.com

About the Editor

Dr. Steve Warner earned his Ph.D. at Rutgers University in Mathematics,

and he currently works as an Associate Professor at Hofstra University. Dr. Warner has more than 20 years of experience in general math tutoring and ACT math and science tutoring. He has tutored students both individually and in group settings and has published many math prep books for the SAT, ACT and AP Calculus exams. Dr. Warner can be reached at

steve@SATPrepGet800.com

BOOKS FROM THE
GET 800 COLLECTION

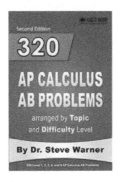
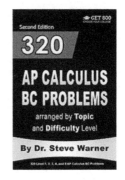

Made in the USA
Middletown, DE
01 July 2021